P9-AOR-932

SI

New Power
for Management

New Power
for Management

COMPUTER SYSTEMS AND MANAGEMENT SCIENCE

David B. Hertz

DIRECTOR, MCKINSEY & COMPANY, INC.

McGraw-Hill Book Company

NEW YORK   ST. LOUIS   SAN FRANCISCO   LONDON
SYDNEY   TORONTO   MEXICO   PANAMA

"Das höchste wäre zu begreifen, dass alles Faktische schon Theorie ist."
—GOETHE

True understanding comes with the realization that everything factual
is, in essence, theory.

*To B. V. H., B. H. B., and V. H. P., my individual
and collective teachers in some significant aspects
of the management sciences.*

Preface

M*AN* is a toolmaker. And tools have given him the power to cope with, and in some cases subdue, the forces of nature. They have enabled him to build and destroy civilizations and to organize and manage the activities connected with his life on this planet. Tools include systems and methods for managing. This book is about management tools—recently developed, powerful tools that, in the hands of alert and perceptive executives, are beginning to shape the paths and destinies of man's instruments of production.

These tools are new implements for management. They are perhaps as significant for today's world as the plow was in early agricultural societies. In one sense, however, they are not new. Management is a universal activity of mankind. Management techniques and methods have been evolving continuously through history. Discoveries and inventions are seldom forgotten, and each opens the way to many others. Double-entry bookkeeping, used over 500 years ago, is but one of many foundation-stone inventions upon which the power of modern management is built.

It is only recently, however, that the potent methods employed in the physical sciences and mathematics have been brought to bear on management problems. World War II saw massive forces —armed with highly complex technology—arrayed in a life or death struggle. Traditional methods of deploying and managing these forces were quickly supplemented by analytical techniques developed by scientists and mathematicians. The process whereby this was done became known as "Operational Research" in Great Britain and "Operations Research" in the United States. In the intervening years, business and industry have drawn upon these developments and supplemented them with others that had been gradually coming into wider use, such as statistical quality control, cost accounting, capital budgeting, and behavioral science.

We have reached a point in time when such methods have become elaborated and applied effectively in almost every aspect of our industrial and institutional life. On the other hand, much of the power of these new tools remains untapped because the understanding necessary for their use is not available at all managerial levels. There has been a large number of excellent publications on the various technical aspects of these developments—linear programming, Monte Carlo and simulation techniques, inventory theory, game theory, queuing theory, and systems analysis, among others. However these publications have been mainly addressed to professional scientists, not to managers. But managers hold the key to successful applications. What is missing is the capability of the executive to put these powerful ideas in place and make them work. I have attempted to fill this need by addressing this book to executives who want to understand what these tools are all about and how they can be used.

The threads of the various scientific developments in management have merged today into what are now called the management sciences. These sciences provide managers with new power and truly effective managers must find a way to understand and apply them. Understanding how they are used is very similar to understanding how to play a better game of poker. The rules of poker are simple, and virtually anyone can play. By following the rules, one can play in a game for any stakes whatever and, with a little luck, not lose everything. But it would be foolhardy to play in a big-time game, merely because one knew the rules of poker. It takes more than just knowing the rules to play a satisfactory, let alone a winning game. Among other things that a scientific investigation of poker can teach are the odds on drawing one kind of hand or another. A novice who does not understand these odds, playing against a person who does, is certainly under a great handicap. He might win, but it is unlikely. Clearly, understanding probabilities is not the only determinant of success. But even knowing the odds can improve decision making and "profit-making potential" to an enormous extent.

Similarly, the methods of the management scientist can be applied to business and can yield an understanding of the "odds" and of the ways to improve decision-making processes of managers at all levels. In addition to analytical methods, the manager can command the power of the computer. The computer is both a tool of the manager and a tool of the management scientist. The computer's technological development has been the key to the progress made in the last decade in the management sciences. Managers can analyze and examine decision problems today that would have been virtually unthinkable only a few years ago. Therefore, I stress the development of computer-based management information systems as one major factor of the new power that these tools give to management.

I have attempted to explain the significance of the management sciences and computer systems in modern business. I have tried to write in language that will be understandable to the executive. Theoretical concepts are of no avail if those who must put them to work do not understand the "how" of them. Therefore, I have included some historical background of the development of computer systems and management science and, more importantly, the ways in which these tools have been used for more effective decision making. I hope, through the use of examples of applications, that this book will provide a basis for understanding how imaginative managers develop and implement new approaches to their problems.

I recognize that business organizations do not always readily accept innovations. Changes can be viewed as either too radical or too costly. Often the need for change is not even admitted. As a result, the techniques employed to accomplish the purposes of an organization are often inappropriate to situations that represent the forces at work in the external world. Of course, if these forces are changing slowly, an organization can take its time about adopting new methods and ideas, for the gap between the old and the new forces is never very large. As change accelerates, however, the gap widens rapidly. Organizations can be quickly left behind. When this gap grows too great and competitors are forging ahead, the organization may become ineffective.

To prevent this in the modern business world, the executive must be able to communicate with and use the talents of management scientists and computer experts. This book was written to try to bridge the communications gap that so often exists between them. I have drawn heavily on my experiences in many organizations over the years since World War II in attempting to make operations research, management science, and computer systems profit-making tools. It has been my good fortune to be associated with institutions that were in the forefront of the development of many of the noteworthy applications that exist today. Much of what I have learned and written about here stems from work carried out in collaboration with colleagues in these organizations. I am indebted to all of them and in the separate acknowledgments have indicated some to whom I owe special thanks. This book reflects many ideas I have expressed in past speeches and papers. Those papers that should be especially singled out are listed.

It is my hope that managers who read this book will come away with an appreciation and an understanding of what can be done with the tools described, and with a feeling of responsibility to achieve major improvements in the effectiveness of our society as a whole. They, themselves, are the only ones who can make the promise of power in these new tools a reality.

David Bendel Hertz

Acknowledgments

I AM grateful to a great many individuals who have helped shape the thoughts and ideas reflected in this volume. I have tried to list in these acknowledgments some, but not all, to whom I owe thanks. Among those who have had particular influence on the development of my personal philosophy of the use of scientific methods in business are the late Professors Walter Rautenstrauch and Robert T. Livingston, and Professors Sebastian B. Littauer, C. West Churchman, Russell L. Ackoff, B. H. P. Rivett, Ronald A. Howard, Harvey M. Wagner, and Robert F. Fetter.

Colleagues with whom I have been associated in my business career and who have helped me work on specific problems—some of which are described in the text—are Professors Phillip G. Carlson, David W. Miller, and Martin K. Starr. Mr. Albert Battersby of Oxford has furnished me with very helpful comments on the first three chapters of this book.

Dr. Richard F. Hespos, Mr. Robert R. Champion, and Mrs. Joan Morthland Bush worked with me at McKinsey & Company on the planning models in Chapter 4 and the risk analysis and investment procedures as outlined in Chapters 5 and 6. (Some of the material in these chapters appeared in similar form in two articles that appeared in the *Harvard Business Review:* "Risk Analysis in Capital Investment" and "Investment Policies That Pay Off." This material was adapted by permission of the *Harvard Business Review.*)

Messrs. Robert A. Hammond and Alan H. Gepfert, also of McKinsey & Company, worked on the logistics examples and the production and distribution analyses described in Chapter 7 during the course of client engagements at McKinsey & Company. Dr. Kurt H. Schaffir of Arthur Andersen & Co. originally developed the ideas on the optimum length of a product line mentioned in Chapter 8. Professor Carlson and I worked together on the style goods information problem mentioned in Chapter 8 at Arthur Andersen & Co.

The material in Chapter 9 on analyzing organization structure was originally presented by me at the NATO and SHAPE Technical Centre Conference on Command and Control Systems in Paris on November 16, 1964. The example in this Chapter draws upon a structure developed by S. Sankar Sengupta and Russell L. Ackoff and presented in a paper entitled "Systems Theory from an Operations Research Point of View" at the Systems Science Conference at the University of Pennsylvania in 1964.

A number of my associates at McKinsey & Company have contributed a great deal to my views as to the best use of computers for management information systems. Specifically, Messrs. R. George Glaser, Jr., Hendrick S. Smith, Ridley Rhind, Gordon P. Smith, and V. Lee Barnes collaborated in preparing the report published by McKinsey & Company entitled "Unlocking the Computer's Profit Potential," some ideas from which are reflected in Chapters 10 and 11.

I am particularly indebted to Professor David W. Miller for his help in the preparation of the Supplementary Reading List.

Messrs. Gene Hawes and Roland D. Mann and Mrs. Janet Glasheen provided the editorial advice, without which this book could not have been written, and I am most grateful to Gene Zelazny for his imaginative and helpful advice in connection with the illustrations in this book. My secretary, Mrs. Susan Burns, has most effectively handled the process of preparing the manuscript for publication.

The quotation from Marshall McLuhan's *Understanding Media* is reprinted with his permission.

I am most grateful to all of the persons mentioned and others, in particular my partners at McKinsey & Company, who have contributed significantly to what I have to say. Of these I must single out Warren M. Cannon and Douglas Watson as being especially helpful. However, I alone am responsible for any mistakes of fact or judgment that may be included in what follows.

David Bendel Hertz

Contents

PREFACE vii

ACKNOWLEDGMENTS xi

1. *Why Management Science?* . . . . . . *I*

Management Science Today. Background of Management Science. Methods and Techniques. Major Business Applications. How to Start Using the Management Sciences.

2. *New Tools for Decision Making* *15*

Algorithms for Decision Making. Key Factors in the Decision Process. Factors That Are Difficult to Quantify. Factors That Can Be Quantified. Management's Continuing Role in Decisions.

3. *Management Information Systems* *30*

Real-time Systems. Simulation Systems. "Optimization" Systems. Implementing the Modern Information System.

4. *Planning Long-range Business Strategy* . . *46*

Planning for Decision Making. Problem Solving. Risk Analysis.

5. Capital Investment Analysis *66*

Need for New Concept.   Sharpening the Picture.   Practical Test.

6. Designing Capital Investment Programs . . *86*

Remaining Investment Planning Problems.   Risk and the Future.   The Function of an Investment Policy.   The Concept of Efficiency.   Probabilistic Long-range Planning.   Conclusion.

7. Production-Distribution-Marketing Analysis *106*

Examples of Progress.   Complete Development of a Coordinated System.   Objectives of the Systems Analysis.   How the Work Was Done.   Making the Analysis Pay Off.   Making Profitable Use of Linear Programming.   Realizing the Payout.   Summary.

8. Building Better Marketing Models . . . *130*

Management Science Solutions to Basic Marketing Problems.   The Demand Pattern in Marketing Strategy.   Problems and Consequences.   Opportunities for the Future.

9. Analyzing Organization Structure . . . *145*

Approaching Organizational Analysis through Management Science.   Organization and the Meaning of Structure.   Definition of Tasks and Objective Functions.   Decision-rule Generation.   Communication Linkages.   Summary.

10. Computer Systems for Management Control *160*

Computer Developments—Past and Future.   Major Developments.   Management Performance.   Examples of Progress.   The Management Science Potential of Time Sharing.

11. The Task for Top Management *179*

Technological.   Managerial.   Steps for Implementing Computer Systems.   The Systems Portfolio.   The Project Plan.   Personnel.   Summary.

SUPPLEMENTARY READING LIST FOR EXECUTIVES **198**

INDEX **203**

CHAPTER 1

Why Management Science?

*I*N an increasingly complex business environment,
management science techniques are providing a growing number
of firms with decisive competitive advantages. These techniques
are achieving even greater effectiveness as they are increasingly
coupled to the expanding power of the computer. In effect, they
help supply the answers to the three basic management questions:
(1) Where are we heading? (2) Where should we be heading? and
(3) How will we get there? Management science techniques can
furnish corporate decision makers with realistic, dollars-and-cents
evaluations of alternative courses of action aimed toward specific
goals, and help shape their decisions accordingly.

In recent years the use of computers has permitted the development of management science applications that until now have
been either too difficult or too expensive to undertake. And computers are successfully being used to implement complex and

sophisticated management systems that could not otherwise have been efficiently administered, such as the warranty systems of the major automobile manufacturers that keep track of individual cars from the time they are entered in the production schedule until the warranty runs out several years, and perhaps several purchasers, later. Thus supported by the computer, the scope and potential of management science in energizing new and imaginative management processes are enormous. Changes will involve not only the information inputs on which major business decisions are based but also the types of decisions analyzed and the significant factors examined in the analyses.

MANAGEMENT SCIENCE TODAY

Management science methods include those derived and applied in operations research such as mathematical programming, critical path scheduling, waiting line theory, business model building, and systems analysis. These methods have been well publicized through their use by large corporations and government agencies. The food processor H. J. Heinz Company, for example, developed new methods to determine the routing of shipments of ketchup from its six plants to seventy warehouses. As a result, direct shipping costs were cut by many thousands of dollars annually. The company later used management science methods to plan its entire warehousing system for all products. SKF Industries has reported savings of over $100,000 a year through production scheduling based on a single application of management science.

Scott Paper has developed a broad-spectrum systems analysis for evaluating proposed new products. It reports that its performance has since been considerably better than the 75 percent to 95 percent failure rate for new-product introductions experienced by the nation's 200 leading packaged-goods manufacturers. Lockheed Aircraft makes extensive use of management science for its long-range economic and sales forecasting. Raytheon uses PERT (performance evaluation and review technique) network scheduling techniques to control large-scale, complex development activities, while Continental Oil and other oil companies use management science techniques to get hard data on the risks and returns of their major capital investment opportunities.

The Ford Motor Company has become especially conspicuous among the many other leading corporations that sharpen their competitive edge through applications of management science techniques. Some of these applications were carried to and expanded at the Department of Defense by Secretary McNamara, a Ford alumnus. General Motors and International Harvester are among the other automotive companies making profitable use of management science and computer systems. General Tire and Rubber and U.S. Rubber also utilize such systems. Every petroleum refinery in the world has been programmed through these techniques to get the most profit out of its process equipment and specific crude oil supplies while meeting customer demands. Leaders in industry after industry are similarly employing management science on a growing scale. In fact, there is virtually no major corporation that has not reported some use of these tools. Although there have been numerous failures, as occur with all innovations and widely used new techniques, the successful applications continue to grow in number, sophistication, breadth, and payoffs.

Use of management science is by no means limited to the nation's biggest businesses. In fact, the payoff ratio can sometimes be higher for a smaller company than for a giant corporation. One medium-sized firm, for instance, frequently changed its single assembly line to accommodate the manufacture, at different times, of twenty models of kitchen sinks. The changeover costs substantially reduced profits until a management science team provided a set of production-scheduling rules, cutting the costs by a third.

A small company that sold a line of portable machines to industrial users applied management science to yet another area—marketing. Concerned over its declining sales, this company assigned a management science expert to examine whether its scheduling of sales calls could be profitably revised. Routinely, its salesmen called on approximately two-fifths of their accounts in any one quarter. The researcher determined that the average account had a 30 percent chance of being inactive if it were *not* called on during a quarter and, if it remained active, would produce only 70 percent as much business during the quarter as it would if it had been called on. The combined difference came to about 50 percent more business from an account that was called on as compared with one not called on. The firm's management thus obtained a really solid justification for significantly increasing routine sales calls on selected accounts and, as a result, reaped a six-figure increase in annual gross sales with a spectacular rise in net profits.

Clearly, management science combined with computer systems has demonstrated its effectiveness. It has, in fact, become so widespread that no executive can afford to ignore its potential. Any executive who fails to develop a general understanding of what it is and fails to learn how to take advantage of it may be endangering not only his company's future but his own. On the other hand, the development and application of management science on a significant scale is just beginning: managers at nearly all levels and in virtually any kind of business can therefore find many new opportunities for using these new tools successfully. The purpose of this book is to describe, in simple terms, the kinds of opportunities and benefits that management science can provide to business today and to sketch the outlines of future developments that promise even greater profit opportunities.

BACKGROUND OF MANAGEMENT SCIENCE

What has already been said suggests that the management sciences have become the most significant of modern approaches to business problem solving. Almost every graduate business school or school of industrial administration or engineering now gives or is actively planning courses in management science or in various related study areas: operations research, quantitative methods, computer systems, and mathematical programming.

Management science (the management sciences) is a fairly new term that is perforce open-ended in scope to accommodate new applications and discoveries. The management science field may be broadly defined to include all bodies of scientific knowledge and technology that prove effective in helping to resolve problems of managing any organization or enterprise. A large part of the management science knowledge that is bringing about fundamental changes in business management today consists of analytic methods of projecting quantitatively the probable results—in terms of costs and revenues (benefits)—of alternative decisions or courses of action taken in complex or uncertain enterprise situations. (A large segment of the management sciences falls under the term "operations research," which includes such branches as linear programming, mathematical programming, network analysis, queuing theory, and search theory.[1])

Operations research techniques, for example, draw on the whole of scientific and experimental methodology; people-oriented (behavioral) sciences are generally considered to be part of the present management science package, since management deals with people. And because the use of computer technology is an intimate part of today's management process, we must look to the systems analysts and computer programmers—and their tool kits—to supply additional underpinnings to the burgeoning new world of management science. Thus, management science knowledge embodies the methodology of scientific research; it also very often incorporates the sophisticated mathematical techniques of scientific research and hence is most frequently put to use through advanced computer systems. Management science, then, is an applied science based on mathematics and the physical, biological, and behavioral sciences.

For all its present uses, management science has not yet come of age. Today's management science applications can be likened to those of cost accounting thirty years ago or of statistical quality control twenty years ago. Each of these tools gradually had to displace more primitive methods and concepts, slowly developing adaptations and applications for all kinds and sizes of businesses, manufacturing firms, extraction enterprises, service activities, and marketing concerns. Now there are cost accounting and quality control approaches to fit every need and every purse, and both of these tools are unquestionably accepted as parts of sound management. This same development is being repeated in the management sciences.

Management science has just begun to develop such diverse ap-

---

[1] Each of these terms represents a branch of analytical or mathematical theory applied to a practical problem: linear programming is used for efficient resource allocation; mathematical programming, which encompasses linear programming as well, is also used for resource allocation, with fewer restrictions on the formulation of the problem; network analysis is used for the sequencing of activities (simplified or special aspects called critical path methods); queuing theory is used for servicing activities, as in check-out counters or airports; search theory is used to effectively locate desirable materials, e.g., ore bodies, customers, submarines.

proaches. Authorities generally agree that management science stems from the advanced statistical methods applied to manufacturing in the late 1930s [2] and that it came into large-scale use as the "operations research" or "operations analysis" of World War II, to help solve the enormously complex new problems of strategic and tactical decisions that faced military staffs. Winston Churchill in 1939 called upon some of Britain's leading scientists to help figure out how the newly invented radar devices (which were in critically limited supply) could best be used to protect England. The problem involved the possible attack routes of German aircraft and their targets, the defending airfields, and the placement of the small number of available radar sets with limited detection ranges. The very best mathematical and scientific brains were able to work out a close-to-optimum placement of those twenty sets, and they were used against the German attackers with decisive effect in the historic air battles that followed.

This kind of problem presented a number of new and complicated technical and operational variables and relationships that the military men were not used to handling and could not "optimize" alone. Operations research (OR) gave them a basis for decision by quantitatively weighing the consequences of an enormous number of possibilities and sorting them into manageable categories.

This quantitative evaluation of the consequences of proposed actions is still the key contribution of today's management science to the executive decision maker.

Other problems solved by military OR groups during World War II involved deployment of antiaircraft fire and the best use of escorts for convoys. United States Navy OR groups developed some innovative convoy escort procedures with spectacular success. It is worth noting that their recommendations—ultimately proven in practice—were counter to the conventional and intuitive answers. In the course of analyzing the problem of searching for and attacking submarines, they also invented the now well-

[2] A pre-World War II application was the use of mathematical techniques at a large department store—Bamberger's in Newark, New Jersey—under the direction of Harold Levenson, a former astronomer and then treasurer of the company, and Dr. Arthur Brown, a mathematician, to help determine the best patterns of store evening hours, to determine advertising effectiveness, and to attack other such merchandising problems.

known branch of mathematical operations analysis called *search theory*. OR groups in the United States and elsewhere undertook numerous assignments, some with more success than others, but all had as common features collaboration between scientists and military men and results stated as quantitative evaluations of alternative solutions to the practical, operational problems at hand.

After the war, OR was used more and more in industry, at first in Britain and then, from about 1950 on, in the United States. Not all the attempts were successful: the military problems and the methods for their solution were seldom similar to commercial problems and solutions, and there was not the same urgency on the part of the researchers and realization of need on the part of the users. Some of the terms that had come out of military experience seemed a little out of place in business, but because "scientific methods" already had an old and honored role in solving business problems, businessmen in general did not consider these approaches novel. Certainly the businessman was used to looking at quantitative information as a basis for his decisions. The term "management science" is more appropriate for the techniques of operations research and similar tools that are starting to emerge than "scientific management"; it signifies, essentially, the various ways that scientists may analyze industrial and institutional management problems. In the early days of applications in business, it became clear that there was something new and useful here, but a number of years passed before a clear way of defining it evolved.[3]

METHODS AND TECHNIQUES

Today a large body of management science techniques continues the original OR tradition. These techniques are focused on the development of analytical models, i.e., logical or mathematical rep-

[3] During those years, the Operations Research Society of America was founded (1953), as was the Institute of Management Sciences (1954). Both have flourished and published professional and managerial journals in the field (*Operations Research,* published bimonthly by the former, and *Management Science,* published monthly by the latter). Many universities began to offer courses and degrees in operations research and management science—among them Case Institute of Technology, Columbia University, Carnegie-Mellon University, University of Pennsylvania, Northwestern, Stanford, University of California, and Massachusetts Institute of Technology. As noted earlier, most major universities today offer degrees or courses in the field.

resentations of a management problem or situation. These models are intended to describe, analyze, and present information concerning the outcomes of alternative courses of action in terms that measure the achievement of stated objectives for government, business, or other institutions. This kind of model building is variously called operations research, operations analysis, systems analysis, or cost-benefit analysis—depending on who is doing it and where it is being done. The purpose of model building is to improve performance through quantitatively and analytically informed decision making. This book will concentrate on model building and its applications to management.

Analytical tools for dealing with uncertainty and complexity. Two branches of mathematics—probability and statistical inference, and higher algebra—form the basis for many applications of management science in industry. Because of their key role and frequent use in model building, it will be helpful to know more about these tools.

The future is always uncertain, and the results of critical decisions often hinge upon the outcome of extremely variable events. Things never happen exactly the same way twice; they will often fluctuate around some average. Probability and statistical mathematics are proven and powerful tools for helping businessmen cope with inherent uncertainty.

This very uncertainty provides the entrepreneur with his opportunities to build new business through taking risks; e.g., to introduce new products, to build inventories, etc. Sales vary from week to week; equipment breakdowns occur at different times; products come off the production line at irregular rates. Uncertainty is universal and lies at the heart of every planning and scheduling problem. The businessman's solution is to provide margins of safety: inventory in the warehouse to meet unexpected demand, spare parts to guard against equipment failure, and stand-by labor to avert production line bottlenecks.

Such margins of safety are expensive. Uncertainty thus brings on real costs as well as potential profits. This is an ideal problem for the mathematics of probability: the measurement and determination of the limits of uncertainty. What are the odds on tossing ten heads in a row? This can be very similar to asking what the chances are of getting ten orders on a given day for an item with a usual demand of one a day. Management science uses statistical methods to determine the margin of safety that must be provided for serving a given probable number of customers within specified cost limits. By using statistical methods that provide means for determining the probability of running out of stock for any given inventory level, one can balance the cost of providing extra inventory against the cost of special handling or loss of sales.

Other problems in which statistical methods are useful as a management science tool include helping management determine how many check-out counters should be provided in supermarkets to avoid long waiting lines, or how many truck-loading positions there should be at shipping platforms. The determination of the best sizes and locations of warehouses and other material-handling facilities can also often be approached through the use of these techniques. And, as will be seen, the concepts of probability and statistical methods play a large role in quantitative analyses of investment alternatives.

The second frequently used branch of mathematics—algebraic or geometric analysis, and specifically linear programming and mathematical programming—deals with the problem of combining many variables or factors to give the combination that best achieves a specific objective. For example, as noted earlier, the best combination of crude oil feedstocks and process methods to yield the most profitable mix of products at a petroleum refinery is today universally determined by linear programming methods. This approach can help businessmen solve extremely complex problems. Management of a modern business involves the need to select from a great many possible courses of action some particular combination that will satisfy in a profitable way a variety of simultaneous technical conditions, constraints on the use of resources, or output requirements.

Thus, a producer of feeds can use any number of combinations of ingredients, each having a different cost (subject to daily changes), to meet the nutrient and bulk requirements of the feeds he markets. These requirements are known, as are the costs; the objective is to produce each feed at its lowest cost to meet the demand and, at the same time, to satisfy the nutritional and other requirements. Once the simple but extensive equations describing these conditions, constraints, and requirements have been written, this problem can be solved directly and simply by means of linear programming. The solution will clearly spell out the least-cost combinations, as well as the costs of any alternatives to the best answer. In addition, linear programming provides the answer to a recurrent problem: What is the value of easing or relaxing a restraint? Given that ingredient X is used in limited quantity in the feed formula because of its limited availability at a certain price, how much would it be worth to pay more for additional X and substitute it for another ingredient in the formula? Or, given that the demand for feed A at price B is limited, how much can it be worth to reduce the price in order to increase demand? These questions and many others are explicitly answered by linear programs.

Linear programming is an extremely versatile tool for determining the best allocation of resources to accomplish an objective. It can be used to provide models that can indicate what products should be made on which machines in a machine shop; how paper rolls can be most economically cut into strips of specified sizes; or what is the most efficient order of steps in building a school, office building, or housing complex. Linear programming has helped the businessman to clearly understand and solve such complex problems—alone or in combination—as keeping costs of production, shipping, or storage at a minimum and maintaining the lowest inventory consistent with customer-service requirements.

MAJOR BUSINESS APPLICATIONS

The kinds of practical models management scientists build for increasing business profits correspond to the different steps of management activity, which include:

- Long-range forecasting
- Short-range forecasting
- Resource allocation
- Activity sequencing
- Acquisition of resources
- Capital investment budgeting

Every businessman, whether his business is large or small, must take a long-range view of the future. Many of the businessman's decisions will, of course, be influenced by the way he assembles and analyzes information about the long-range future. To ascertain the likely consequences of alternative courses of action, the management scientist develops models that assemble and analyze such key information as product demand, activity of competitors, price changes, and cost patterns.

A businessman must also develop ways of looking at the near future: tomorrow, next week, next month. Again, he has to have some way of deciding how much inventory to stock, how many people to hire, how much cash to have on hand. Many accounting and control methods are used to this end, but management science is especially helpful when the situation is uncertain and complicated by many factors; for example, management science helps the businessman establish methods for setting inventory levels to meet desired customer service when demand is uncertain.

As we have seen, another problem area for which everyone has some kind of system, and in which management science has been particularly helpful, is the allocation of resources. Under this heading we can include assignment of repair crews to various breakdowns to minimize total costs of labor, materials, and downtime; release of orders to plants or machines; distribution of raw materials among processing units; and countless similar functions.

In addition to assigning resources to requirements, the businessman must decide on the sequence of activities that he, his machines, and his personnel will carry out. And he would like to do this at the best level of profitability. In other words, he must specify who does what and when it is to be done. Routing of trucks, control of construction and maintenance projects, assignment of salesmen's routes, scheduling of machine operations—these are a few of the many applications of management science methods for sequencing activities.

Another kind of problem that businessmen face is the acquisition of resources: raw materials, machines, spare parts, or people. Often much efficiency can be gained through the use of the new techniques in providing cost and benefit information for such purposes as commodity buying, replacing equipment, and determining relative efficiencies of new plants or various combinations of new machines.

These problem areas are closely related. For example, short- and long-range forecasting certainly are involved in resource balancing, activity sequencing, and resource acquisition; and ultimately, in how overall capital investment models can be built and used. With this in mind, one can appreciate how the introduction of new and improved techniques in any of these areas can spread benefits through an entire company.

Management science techniques can thus be used to build mathematical models to aid decision makers in large and small companies alike. As we have seen, the kinds of questions that these models will help answer are:

- What capital investment projects should be accepted?
- How much money should the company tie up in inventory?
- To what extent should larger orders be used to take advantage of quantity discounts?
- How can plant capacity be utilized in combination with fluctuating demand to maintain lowest overall production cost?
- How should production be scheduled—by machine or process?
- How should a construction or maintenance project be scheduled?
- How does the cost of maintenance and repairs change over the life of a piece of equipment and how will its resale value probably change?
- What are the most economical means of transportation, the most economical warehouse and delivery routing patterns?

The models created to answer such problems specify how costs and revenues will be affected by alternative operating decisions under a given set of management policies and specific market, and other external, conditions. They can also indicate how alternative management policies, external conditions, contingency plans, and other variable factors would affect the economic performance of the company. Management science analyses can provide insight into the relations between operating conditions, business performance, and the decision-making processes. In practical terms, they often identify the courses that will minimize costs and maximize income.

HOW TO START USING THE MANAGEMENT SCIENCES

How can a firm, particularly a small firm, begin to realize the benefits of management science? In the first place, sound results require sound data. In making decisions, there is no substitute for comprehensive, accurate documentation. The information house must therefore be in order if anything is to be gained from detailed analyses. In their initial stages, management science projects often pinpoint the fact that insufficient information is available before the time comes to draw on these data. In some cases, the missing information can frequently be retrieved but often at the cost of added expense and delays.

Once a solid information base is assured, how can a company acquire an adequate management science capability? The most usual approach is to develop an in-house technical staff. A company can enroll one or more of its own staff, preferably men with background in physical science and mathematics, in some of the easily accessible university courses and seminars that deal with management science techniques. After this formal training period, the company can allow the trainees to learn and develop skills on the job, assigning them relatively easy projects under the guidance of a sympathetic high-level executive. Or a company can hire one or more graduates of one of the previously mentioned management science programs offered at business schools and engineering colleges. Again, the company might have to give the new employee time to learn and develop skills and thorough understanding of the business.

Another approach is to use outside help. Management science consultants can be found in almost any part of the world today. Before selecting one, however, management should gain some basic understanding of management science techniques and attempt to define the key corporate problem areas. Then it should appoint at least one knowledgeable executive to help the outsider. The proper choice of a consultant is, of course, extremely important; checking with the candidate's former and present clients and discussing potential consultants with key management scientists in academic institutions will prove helpful.

Management must realize that it will get more for its money if it allows its own personnel or a consultant enough calendar time—as opposed to continuous time—to lay the groundwork and let operating personnel integrate the new tasks into their regular activities.

Top-management involvement and support is a virtually essential element in any management science program. The chief executive (or another key management representative) should take a continuing interest in the venture and support it fully. Such support has almost always been a key element in securing a satisfactory payout from such costly man-machine systems as computers. This support is also equally vital for management science man-method systems, and its absence can severely lessen the chances of a program's success.

Management science techniques, in sum, are practical tools that can be used to solve problems faced by most companies, regardless of size. They can no longer be viewed in any sense as "blue-sky" theorizing. Their wide and successful use puts these questions squarely before each executive: "Are the data and information on which you base your decisions as good as your competitors'? Are they the best that can be developed?"

CHAPTER 2

New Tools
for Decision Making

THE effective use of management science, as described in general terms in Chapter 1, greatly changes the content and structure of the management decision-making process in business and government. This can have an almost traumatic effect on some executives, giving them the unsettling feeling that decision making is being taken out of their experienced hands and turned over to an impersonal machine. Even more unsettling, even to those who understand that scientific decision procedures increase rather than reduce the scope of creative intuition, is the sheer range of problems to which management science can be applied— a range so great that it ultimately takes in virtually all of a company's or institution's activities.

Experienced executives are indeed justified in believing that increasing use of management science methods will substantially change the way decisions are made in their companies. Some decisions they used to make will no longer be worth their time. On the other hand, careful reflection will make it abundantly clear that man-made decisions have not become obsolete. On the contrary, there will be more human decisions, even more comprehensive and exciting, to be made. As we shall see in the next chapter, these decisions will have greater significance and will require greater effort and more creativity than ever before. The creative executive's scope of operation will be expanded, not diminished. Further, the ability of the hard-hitting, results-oriented organization to achieve its objectives effectively and efficiently will be enormously enhanced. And such organizations will be more exciting places to work than those that have ignored the potential of the management sciences and computer systems.

Because fear among executives can so easily balk a company's efforts to benefit from management science, it is important to understand how management sciences and computers actually do affect corporate decision making. Scientific, nonintuitive methods can gradually change the structure of decisions at the executive level, making some routine and eliminating them from successively higher management levels, and substituting for them entirely new and potentially more creative decisions. Thus, the executive is freed to devote himself to decisions of more significance and scope.

Continuous load dispatching in an electric utility provides a good historical example. In an electric utility, boilers and generators are cut in and out and turbines are loaded or shut down as actual and projected loads change from hour to hour, or even from minute to minute. The profitability of a utility company is directly affected by load dispatching decisions. Yet it is not likely that management would make these load dispatching decisions today because they are being made much better by automated methods. It will be instructive to examine how load dispatching has evolved from "executive" to "automated" decisions.

In the era of the small, local electric utility with a few generators and power units, changes in load were met (or not met) by imprecise adjustments, often after consultation or discussion with management. As systems grew larger and more complex, economic and engineering analyses of the profitablility of various kinds of load control became common, and the load dispatchers began to assume more and more of the prerogative of deciding how to accommodate the changes. Management simply indicated the objectives, restrictions, and policies that it desired the load dispatchers to meet or follow.

Using tools similar to those of today's management scientists, utility managements soon began to develop means to record and analyze the results of past decisions and to better define the economics—thermal and electrical—of alternative choices in a given situation. The development and codification of these methods suggested that the load dispatcher could be replaced in part by a computer. The result was one of the earliest computerized management applications.

The next step was for the load dispatcher's job to become simply the supplying of the necessary parameters into a computer that, acting on current operating data, either indicates or actually makes the best load allocations under the circumstances. Management no longer even suggests the parameters. The new, important management task is, of course, to decide whether to buy a bigger and better automatic load analyzer and to tie more units into an integrated network. Such decisions, based on the ability to analyze the pattern of probable demands and evaluate the probable economic and technical effects on a very complex system, are of a higher order than earlier ones.

Some of the important management science techniques actually stem from work done in utility and communications systems analysis. The phrase "systems analysis," commonly used to describe some applications of management science, probably owes its origin to this field (rather than to the area of office "systems and procedures").

Gradually up until World War II and very rapidly since, quantitative methods have been extended to ever larger areas of management decision making. Empirical knowledge of cost/revenue relationships has been increasing; so has theoretical understanding of the economic effects of decisions. Analytical methods, or *algorithms,* have been developed for quantitative evaluation of alternative decisions. Computers programmed for management science approaches have begun to be routinely applied to specific situations. And, as a result, management has begun to get greater profit leverage from better and more timely decisions.

Together, these developments are slowly shifting the emphasis of top-management decision making from simply deciding upon specific operating alternatives to the more complex and more rewarding approach of selecting the means for applying methods of analyzing decisions problems, choosing among alternative analyses, and finally determining ways of implementing the results of the analyses. Since the manner in which these analyses result in algorithms, or "rules," for decision making seems to be the key to improved decisions, examples will be helpful.

ALGORITHMS FOR DECISION MAKING

An algorithm is simply a set of rules for carrying out some numerical calculation that is intended to yield the same result no matter by whom or when applied. Thus, rules for ordinary arithmetic— e.g., addition, subtraction, division—are algorithms. There can, of course, be different algorithms for the same operation: for example, performing long division and finding square roots. Computers are generally used to apply algorithms to decision problems.

The choice among algorithms that accomplish exactly the same numerical operation is a matter of convenience and efficiency, but the choice among those management science algorithms aimed at providing decision rules for the same management objective can be a serious decision that will require an understanding of the underlying problem and of the management science process.[1]

The important factors from the business point of view are:

▪ The application of the underlying operation or process

▪ The existence of an algorithm or set of decision rules for handling the operation

Consider a simple and familiar example. Addition is an operation for which an effective set of rules (an algorithm) provides

---

[1] A simple example might be alternative decision rules (algorithms) for determining how much inventory to stock. Rule 1 might be: "Replenish each month end to the maximum monthly demand of the past 6 months." Rule 2: "Replenish to four times the average of the two peak weekly demands whenever stock falls to a preset minimum." The determination of cost difference between these two sets of rules in terms of inventory carrying costs, out-of-stock penalties, and production and procurement costs, is clearly not a matter of simple intuition.

swift and consistent results. It is also a very useful and important operation for the businessman. The addition algorithm is so much a part of our thinking that we are hardly aware of its effect on decision making, but it provides a good example through which to consider the possibility of improving management decisions.

We all know that addition and subtraction form an integral part of an accounting system. Business decisions would be difficult indeed without some means of measuring resources and liabilities, which is fundamentally what accounting systems do. Thus, addition (or subtraction, its logical equivalent) enables a businessman to determine, for example, whether a spending decision is feasible and how much of a drain upon his resources it will be. He cannot find *conceptual* answers to this general kind of problem without the *idea* of addition or subtraction, and he cannot find the actual or *concrete* answers without rules—algorithms. The addition process applied in the accounting system thus furnishes both significant concepts and key information about the state of one's affairs and provides a basis for decision. It illustrates the importance of the development of the ideas about decision rules and the basic processes underlying quantification in decision making.

Imagine, if you can, doing business without using addition and subtraction.[2] Every time a businessman wanted to make a purchase, he would have to devise somehow a way of determining whether the price would or would not exceed his resources! Such a situation is virtually impossible to conceive because the modern business world is so dependent on the use of reasonably common accounting *concepts* and *algorithms* for handling double-entry bookkeeping. The algorithms used in accounting go considerably beyond addition and subtraction and are worth pursuing one step further to gain additional insight into the process of combining experience and algorithms (decision rules) into *models* that describe some aspect of the physical world.

Accounting ideas have evolved more or less continuously for 5,000 years. Almost five hundred years ago, Pacioli, the father of modern accounting, wrote the definitive treatise on double-entry bookkeeping and how it provides a detailed representation of the business situation. His stated purpose was "to give the trader without delay information on his assets and liabilities." Double-entry

---

[2] It has been done in some cultures!

bookkeeping was then a profound concept for decision makers and thus a great social invention. Prior to that point in time, each decision for a commitment, division of profits, or other significant problem required the businessman to laboriously figure out where he stood. Double-entry bookkeeping is, of course, still with us in much the same form, and the concept remains basic to business accounting almost everywhere.

Herein lies the key point: the importance of really significant new concepts is not so much that they may be applied effectively in several situations but that they can, like double-entry bookkeeping, be used by all businesses. Management science plays a unique and critical role, representing generally applicable abstractions of real-life structural interrelationships and economic concepts. These ideas can thus serve as versatile, easily handled tools whose use can become nearly automatic.

KEY FACTORS IN THE DECISION PROCESS

Representations of key business processes, implemented by algorithms and applied to specific operations activities or parts of a business—models—are the fundamental building blocks of management sciences and computer systems. To use a model to help make decisions, it is of course essential to quantify the elements of the decision process included in the model: what we hope to achieve is essentially a statement of the profit and loss consequences of alternative courses of actions. A look at the total decision process shows what management has to do to quantify its elements.

Key factors underlying business decisions are:
- Resources at hand
- Possible alternatives
- Commitments required for alternatives
- Results (costs incurred, revenues or benefits received) to be achieved from alternatives
- Interactions between alternatives chosen and prior and later choices

Pacioli's algorithm for double-entry bookkeeping was a major step in quantifying the first element—resources at hand. Over the intervening 500 years, businessmen, assisted by economists and other specialists, have labored to give expression to concepts and algorithms that would attach consistent and reliable numbers to the other elements. They have succeeded in limited areas of specific business operations, as the example of electric power load dispatching illustrates. But until recently, very few new universals have been developed. Break-even analysis, cost accounting, and quality control are among the few examples of the type of conceptual and quantifiable tools that lend themselves to more or less universal use.

The inherent difficulties involved in quantifying alternatives, the results to be achieved from choices, and the interaction of past and future choices can hardly be exaggerated. Assuming that the resources and the commitments required for a set of available alternatives could be clearly described, the real problem for the business decision maker still remains. He needs to be able to analyze *consistently* and *quantitatively* the net effects of applying his resources.

This does not mean that the description will be either deterministic or final. Ultimately it will (and must) be dynamic and have characteristics of uncertainty. As Matthew Arnold put it, "They who await no gift from chance have conquered fate." Changes in the environment and changes in the uncertainty with which the future is viewed will determine the parameters or guiding variables that must be fed into analytical procedures for modern decision making through computer-based management science models. Thus, the feedback relationship between the organization and its environment will always be an integral part of these problem-solving approaches.

Finally, complete dependence on analytical methods is a dangerous course. The successful executive's job is to provide a synthesis using the most accurate, complete, and precise results of analysis possible but also including still unquantifiable elements (and there always will be some!).

Before proceeding to what *can* be quantified in the decision process, the kinds of resources, commitments, and results that are difficult to measure in consistent numerical terms should be examined.

FACTORS THAT ARE DIFFICULT TO QUANTIFY

The effective decision maker cannot neglect the difficult but critically important measurement of such resources as:

- Executive talent
- Research and development
- Advertising
- Management information systems
- Inertia of the company relative to the economy

Meaningful estimates of the potential results of critical decisions require some evaluation of those elements. Attempts to describe these kinds of variables quantitatively have yet to prove completely rewarding. In these areas the executive is caught up in a web of personal, psychological actions and reactions that limit his ability to establish meaningful hypotheses. Plans are usually judged by results. Thus, little or nothing can be known about the future value of the plans themselves. In planning for management succession, for example, a company may hire many management trainees and rely on statistical odds to produce a highly competent president some years later—or it may wish to take its chances on developing one through hiring three new vice-presidents. The difference to the company of either plan may be very great, but it cannot yet be predicted quantitatively through a meaningful model —since either plan will produce *a* president.

In any case, the development of algorithms for decision making cannot be effectively carried into areas where satisfactory measurements do not apply. Business is a part of life, and as Justice Hughes wrote: "Life is a painting, not a sum." However, the fact that ultimate decisions are human, not mechanical, should not preclude management's exploration of those areas of business where inputs, relationships, and consequences can be analyzed and measured and thus understood.

FACTORS THAT CAN BE QUANTIFIED

Managers often feel that alternatives in some of the areas in which they can make decisions are so few that they have little or no choice when decision problems arise. In other words, their decisions are already dictated by the restraints placed upon them internally and externally. When this is true, the restrictions can usually be described quantitatively and often precisely. When quantitative restrictions dictate alternative courses of action, decision making becomes an automatic process and there is no need for managerial intervention. Very often, proven models with well-developed algorithms exist for such restricted problems; an example is inventory reorder policy in simple demand situations.

However, in most cases, even where executives feel that few improvements can be made in the decision process, a detailed analysis of the problem area in which the decision is to be made reveals a surprising number of alternative choices.

When the problem is complex, and the outcome of one's choices is uncertain, many managers feel that the best one can do is a common-sense guess. Yet, as we saw in Chapter 1, these are precisely the circumstances where management science techniques are most valuable. When basic inputs are readily measurable, models using some tested algorithms can take both characteristics into account. A manager's belief that he can rely on sheer intuition may therefore needlessly keep him from achieving the best possible economic performance for his business.

The effects of uncertainty can frequently be reduced significantly and occasionally the amount of uncertainty as well. A simple example is a company that was considering entrance into a new market. Instead of making a difficult and uncertain forecast of the market share it was likely to win, management set out to determine what share of market would be needed to earn a satisfactory return on the investment. Analysis showed that the answer was close to 40 percent—a far larger share of market than the company was at all likely to attain for the money it was prepared to allot to the venture. The idea was therefore abandoned.

Where the problem of uncertainty cannot be significantly reduced, it can usually be attacked through a careful analysis of the "true" uncertainty surrounding the outcomes of individual courses of action.[3] This kind of analysis is illustrated in the development of information to help decide on an investment in new

---

[3] This is equivalent to estimating the odds that a specific event or class of events will occur: e.g., figuring that there is a 1-out-of-5 chance that the dollar will be devalued, or that there is a 2-out-of-3 chance that a given project will do better than break even.

facilities. To develop this data, a broad range and mix of many variable factors must be analyzed. This work can be done by management of the divisions involved; e.g., marketing, engineering, and production. The problem, however, is that while the studies will indicate various factors of uncertainty, they will not show how these factors can be combined to permit realistic evaluation of the several probable end results of the investment. The estimates of the many variables that significantly influence the outcome of an investment will, at best, fall within some range of error, even if the estimates are not biased in one direction or the other. Statistically speaking, a good estimate of any one of these variables is what might be called "a 50 percent estimate," that is, an estimate in which the chances are 50-50 that the actual result will fall above or below the estimated quantity. For example, if the cost of introducing a new product line is estimated at $2.3 million, there would be 1 chance in 2 that the actual cost would be greater than $2.3 million and 1 chance in 2 that it would be less. The cost would only coincidentally turn out to be exactly $2.3 million.

Such a 50 percent estimate is perhaps the "best" single estimate that can be made under the circumstances,[4] although from a management point of view, it may be an undesirable estimate on which to base a decision. Whether or not this estimate is useful for management decision making depends on three things: (1) the range of possible error in the estimates; (2) the odds of being above or below the estimate by specified amounts; and (3) the gain or penalty attached to being above or below the estimate by a given amount. For example, suppose that a company estimates annual sales of a new plant at $100 million. If the annual sales estimate is needed for making a management decision, the 50 percent estimate will be a suitable basis for the decision only if the following conditions are approximated: (1) the chances of deviating from the estimates by specified amounts are approximately the same in either direction (for example, the odds of achieving at least $90 million in sales are the same as the odds of achieving $110 million); and (2) the penalty for achieving sales of $90 million is the same as the gain for

---

[4] Note that it is not necessarily the most likely result; thus, if the possible costs ranged from $1 million to $3.6 million and each of the values between these ranges was equally likely to occur, the 50 percent estimate would still be $2.3 million, but there would be no single most likely value.

$110 million (for example, profit is reduced by $1 million if the lower figure is achieved and is increased by $1 million if the higher figure is achieved).

However, to continue with this example, the 50 percent estimate will not provide a satisfactory basis for a management decision under other conditions. Suppose that (1) the chances of achieving at least $90 million in sales are 6 out of 10, and the chance of achieving at least $110 million is only 1 out of 10; (2) if sales of $90 million are achieved a break-even point is reached; and (3) if $110 million is achieved, $1.5 million in profits is gained over the $10 million profits estimated for sales of $100 million. That is (assuming a $10 million profit at the $100 million level):

Sales Estimate	$90 million	$100 million	$110.0 million
Profit	0	$ 10 million	$ 11.5 million
Odds	6/10	5/10	1/10
Chance of achieving or bettering estimate	60%	50%	10%

Under these circumstances, a management decision based on the 50 percent estimate could be very risky. There is a 40 percent chance of not selling more than $90 million; the chances of achieving $110 million in sales are small; and even if a $110 million sales level were reached, the added profits would be only $1.5 million. For each of the major variables entering into an investment decision—production cost, sales price, etc.—such uncertainties usually exist.

In such situations, rules can be developed and computer programs applied to aid management in consistently and quantitatively analyzing the likely outcomes of various courses of action. Examples are given in later chapters. This method simulates the possible courses of future events in a computer and analyzes the results. The simulation method of analyzing potential decisions, which can take both uncertainty and complexity into account, is becoming widely known and used. In this case, a "model" of the capital investment decision process is developed to help management to choose the best alternative under the particular conditions of uncertainty.

Where there are known interactions among the variables and where there are significant restrictions on the resources available to management, the best ways to use the resources to attain specific objectives can be found by other important concepts and models —of which linear programming,[5] briefly characterized in the opening chapter, is a most important and widely used example.

In one sense, linear programming can be considered an extension and extraordinary development of double-entry bookkeeping, because linear programming keeps track in a completely balanced manner of all quantified inputs and outputs of the production or economic system under consideration. However, linear programming is far more than this. In another sense, it may be described as a way of analyzing the use (not merely the existence) of resources to find the combinations that would produce results to fit specific management objectives, such as profit maximization or cost minimization (for example, the lowest cost raw materials mix to produce a given product in a chemical plant).

A linear programming description of a management problem makes it possible to explore the profit and loss consequences of a large number of alternative interacting decisions. Given the basic assumptions of an allocation-of-resources problem, it is possible to show by linear programming what the best allocation would be and then to demonstrate, by conventional profit and loss accounting, that there is no better allocation.

Consider the example of an oil company that purchases crude oil from a number of sources, processes this oil at a number of refineries, and delivers the product from the refineries to a number of locations geographically dispersed. Such a company faces a continuing set of decision problems. The oil it can purchase is of varying composition and price. The refineries that can process the oil have various kinds of equipment in various states of repair. Hence, they can produce different end products from the different crudes with varying degrees of efficiency. The refineries can also deliver to a number of points, each of which has its own particular combination of product requirements.

The use of a linear programming model, an algorithm to solve the numerous equations involved, and a computer to do the necessary arithmetic provides management with a tool very similar to that discussed earlier in connection with the load analyzer for elec-

[5] Linear programming techniques are discussed in greater detail in Chap. 7, pp. 117–123.

tric power plants. With the changing input of prices, demands, and efficiencies, it is possible to calculate the following important variables on an instantaneous or on a projected basis: (1) the marginal value of a particular type of crude; (2) the marginal value of any specific kind of equipment in the refineries; and (3) the marginal cost of any product at any specific location. As indicated earlier, refinery managements today use the model, various algorithms, and computers to make such calculations and to control refinery operations accordingly.

Until the linear programming model and the algorithm to solve it were available, such calculations were literally impossible. Linear programming and similar models base their strength on the fundamental concept of efficient allocations of resources to meet management objectives and to satisfy other constraints and requirements imposed on the system. The power and utility of these computer-based analyses are essentially the same as the power and utility of ordinary arithmetic. Without these tools decision making is awkward and perhaps inefficient. With them, management can weigh key decisions in a rigorous and scientific manner.

MANAGEMENT'S CONTINUING
ROLE IN DECISIONS

In the oil company example just cited, the fact that the relative value of a specific crude or the relative cost of a specific product can be determined at any given time certainly would be influential in the making of specific decisions. There is a competitive advantage in knowing these facts because they show certain decisions to be inevitable. The company that knows these facts and can recognize the decisions that are inevitable will move ahead. In the ordinary economic sense, this will force others to follow. Therefore, management can look forward to an inevitably continuing and growing use of profit-making tools such as this.

But the question remains whether management decision making has in fact been automated when such tools are used. The answer to this is "no"; rather, the environment in which decisions are made has changed. Decision making moves to a new and perhaps more difficult level. Management, then, has increased its theoretical understanding of the economics of decision making and has available for continuing use some models and algorithms that apply these understandings to specific problems. Management now faces the job of making choices among models and improving the use of these models, much as it improved the use of addition and double-entry bookkeeping.

Will management decision making be entirely automated in the future? The answer is simply that a decision which can be truly automated is no longer really a management function. Management will continue to "make decisions" no matter what algorithms are supplied by the management scientist. In all effective leadership there will be decision making; this will be apparent both to the decision maker and to those who are affected by the decision. Management will retain the power of choice, of having and using preferences (for specific models, for example), and of resolving to apply specific results of model analyses in given situations. In a sense, its power will be even greater, for its understanding will be deeper and its grasp of situations more comprehensive.

On the other hand, with management inevitably utilizing these new decision-making concepts, models, and calculating mechanisms, the environment in which management analyzes and chooses is changed; the language that management speaks is changed; and even familiar events, seen in new perspective, seem different. A refinery manager using a linear programming model to schedule his runs looks at his refinery in an entirely different manner than do managers who are not familiar with this technique. In fact, it is no longer possible for him to "go back" to the old ways of making production run decisions. Perhaps the most significant change is not the results from the computer runs of the linear program but this new way of looking at the production process. The competitive power of increased understanding and increased ability to measure, quantify, and analyze effectively is so great that all managers will sooner or later be caught up by it, just as the entire business world was caught up by double-entry bookkeeping.

The major impact of management science, in summary, has been to force management to face new kinds of decisions on a new level of decision making with new forms of information. One of the new required decisions is the establishment of rules for logical analysis. For example, a modern inventory system model requires

—as old systems did not—that management set specific policies that define the operating parameters of the system.

Management science techniques coupled with effective computer systems provide today's managers with timely, accurate, and relevant information that permits them to cut through the complexities and uncertainties of business situations and thereby to select strategies and tactical courses of action and to exercise control with greater confidence in the outcome than ever before. Competitive advantages such as wider profit margins, lower costs, faster service or production, higher quality, and larger returns on investment are the payoffs from these improved information systems that rely on the combined power of a scientific approach and the capabilities of modern computing machinery.

CHAPTER 3
Management
Information Systems

I_F modern information systems help make good managers better, then bad information is a major obstacle to effective management of any kind. Too often, information available to management is plentiful without being relevant, extensive without being adequate, and detailed without being precise. Its seeming comprehensiveness is illusory and, although it flows in without respite, it is not timely. In short, it is less a help than a hindrance to effective decision making and control.

These problems can be overcome or greatly alleviated through the new management science developments discussed in the first two chapters. In the past, management has had to rely on data that often did not adequately portray the risks, opportunities, and potential consequences of alternative decisions and actions. Today, however, as we have seen, it should be possible to design management information systems that will not only provide management with improved forecasts and projections but will also point the way toward courses of action that will achieve optimum results.

Because such management information systems [1] now represent the most effective means of applying management science methods, executives of small as well as large companies should understand how to use them. Opportunities for their application exist in firms of all sizes; the principles are the same, and various kinds of computing facilities exist in scaled-down versions for all types of applications.

The major new developments in information systems have already altered much of management's behavior, if only indirectly. The extent and consequences of these changes may be far greater than is generally realized. Information that has been made available as a result of these new ways of dealing with past events and current decisions has perceptibly changed the actions and thought patterns of many executives.

For example, the "economic pause" of 1962 (or "quasi-recession," as it came to be called) probably approached the severity of a real depression more closely than any previous slump in United States business history. In the words of the *New York Times* (May 20, 1963): [2] "Things that usually happen before a recession happened last year. Profits slipped . . . the rate of inventory accumulation fell off . . . new orders for durable goods slipped . . . the stock market plunged . . . the factory workweek started shrinking . . . wholesale prices weakened . . . the rate of unemployment rose . . . industrial production flattened. . . . All that was missing was the big drop. . . . It was a near miss." The missing drop may be explained differently by economists, but all agree that business executives were receiving a greater amount of timely, de-

---

[1] "System" in this sense, readers should note, means the network of analytical methods and their supporting data bases that management uses in order to keep informed about past, ongoing, and potential operations. It obviously differs from the common meaning of "system" as used by computer manufacturers, who understand a computer system or an information-handling system to be the hardware (and internal operating software) of a particular data-processing installation. "System" is used most often in this book in the former sense, though occasional uses of it in the sense of a particular installation are employed without special explanation when the sense will be clear from the context. It is also used in its common sense, as in referring to a company's distribution system.

[2] © 1963 by The New York Times Company. Reprinted by permission.

tailed, and accurate information than ever before in the economic history of any society. It may be difficult to determine the exact influence of this information, but it contributed significantly to the reversal of the downward trend in that year. It has since been instrumental in maintaining near equilibrium in the economy.[3] Undoubtedly, most businessmen were vaguely aware that they were acting differently than in the past, but few if any realized how profoundly new management science and computer techniques were influencing their behavior—and, as a result, the entire economy.

A main factor in the changes that have taken place is the steadily decreasing unit cost of maintaining, manipulating, and handling information relating to the detailed transactions of a business or government enterprise. In the past decade it has been possible, by investing large amounts of capital, to replace labor in management information systems. Data-processing jobs that were previously far too costly are now economically feasible because of advances in devices for acquiring, manipulating, and communicating information. Information can now be maintained and processed by methods similar to straight-line production. Human error can be reduced; timeliness can be increased; completeness can be assured; and the data can be presented in a form tailored to the management problems at hand. Advances in communications systems have also made it feasible to use on-line and real-time information processing to control production and marketing activities in far-flung enterprises.

In particular, three new kinds of management information systems are significantly altering executive behavior and, to some extent, affecting the economic environment.

1. *"Command and control"* systems [4] employ highly integrated, fast, direct information processing and dissemination. They include both broadly based information structures (such as those used to control a nationwide consumer goods distribution network) and real-time systems used to control operations (such as a

---

[3] And even affecting the key economic decisions of ponderous and politically oriented governmental activities.

[4] A phrase borrowed from military usage to cover a wide range of rapid and extensive systems for acquiring, storing, transmitting, and displaying tactical and operating data.

refinery control computer complex or the load dispatching system described earlier).

2. *Simulation systems* reproduce real-life situations in the computer, permitting the analysis and display of complex time and uncertainty interrelationships for planning and decision making. (They aid, for example, the analysis of capital investment alternatives.)

3. *Optimization systems* usually employ formal mathematical models for evaluating alternative policies and procedures (for example, linear programming applied to refinery resource allocations). Such systems can provide the bases for setting policies as well as for making operating decisions.

These new tools, used singly and in combination, and the resulting new departures in management information systems have materially changed the work done by management. Historically, a manager either determined strategy and made tactical decisions or directly controlled people or machines. Now, as information-handling devices take over an increasing number of routine functions, the many former everyday line management problems tend to disappear. At the same time, the number of decision and strategy problems increases as the span of choice among alternative ways of exercising control expands. As a result, there may be a future decrease in the number of line managers and a corresponding increase in staff personnel.

An observation made by the late President Kennedy in his 1961 budget message reflected the new capability for meeting the challenge of organized complexity that all executives now face. Though he spoke of military management, his thoughts applied equally to business. President Kennedy said that new emphasis must be placed on "improved command and control—more flexible, more selective, more deliberate, better produced. . . . These recommendations are only the beginning of a major but absolutely vital effort to achieve a truly unified, nationwide, indestructible system to assure high-level command, communications, and control. . . ." Applied to industry, this statement indicates a growing need for executives to rely on new methods of obtaining, interpreting, and communicating the data on which strategic and operating plans and decisions are based. In the process, a new kind of manager is emerging. Increased reliance on information that has been generated in accordance with prior scientific analysis and systems design—information computer-produced and processed by formal simulation or optimization models—is bringing those who creatively use the new quantitative methods closer and closer to the heart of the business decision-making process and to top-level responsibilities.

Some new departures exert so revolutionary an influence on their environments that it may be impossible for an organization to survive without using them. One development that perhaps typifies the new powers provided for management by management sciences and computer systems is the so-called "real-time" information processing; "real-time" means "in-time-to-take-effective-action" (e.g., the military command and control system).

REAL-TIME SYSTEMS

Time is always a basic factor in decision systems because there is necessarily a time lapse between information inputs and action outputs. This lapse can vary from a fraction of a second to days, weeks, months, or even years, depending upon the system under consideration. Importantly, however, management can always control the duration of the time lapse beyond some irreducible minimum by the design of a specific information system—a "real-time" system. The U.S. Department of Defense defines a real-time system as a "system whose inputs can influence outputs within a time when the change is still significant." [5] For example, a management decision system operates in real time if the time that elapses between input of data concerning an event (e.g., transaction) and output of corrective action or information does not exceed the time span specified for the requirements of the particular system. Thus, although the load dispatching system for electric utilities has a different minimum time between input and output than does an inventory control system for a steel mill, both, if properly designed, might be said to operate in "real time."

Real-time computer system developments and their future potential have received an extraordinary amount of publicity, frequently fanciful. As a result, such systems are often thought of as

[5] Not instantaneously, as one might infer from some of the futuristic literature about management information systems.

complex networks, replete with costly, exotic devices that can instantly do anything for anybody. Actually, the systems are much simpler and also much less expensive than is often supposed. Real-time systems need only match in speed and complexity the external events to which they must respond. In fact, the systems could as well be called "useful-time" as "real-time."

Speed and complexity requirements of real-time systems are greatest when the tasks they must perform require split-second accuracy and response. Extreme examples include such tasks as monitoring the launching of space vehicles into precise orbits or controlling a cyclotron. In those situations, keeping pace can mean responding to external signals in millionths of a second. Less critical, but still demanding, real-time operations include airline reservation systems and systems for reporting stock exchange prices as fast as transactions occur. In the latter case, trades are based on price data provided by the preceding trades. Therefore, traders, whose objective is to profit through continuous buying and selling, want to obtain this information with minimum delay. Their requirements have provided significant incentives for the development of advanced and sophisticated information-handling and display systems. Ticker tape networks, display consoles, even racetrack tote boards, are examples of the use of real-time (or as close to real-time as human intervention will permit) information for decision making. Improvements are constantly being made in such systems.

Few business decisions, however, require the almost instantaneous event-by-event reporting and response needed for spacecraft launches, financial speculation, or betting on the ponies. For instance, mutual fund managers have little need for event-by-event reporting, even though they operate on the same exchanges as do the speculators. If these investors are to make meaningful decisions, they must have data from individual transactions that are grouped and smoothed. This does not mean that the responses they get are "slow" but rather that, to be meaningful for their purposes, the significant data require longer time spans for both input and output. This difference in the use of the same information suggests that the input-output cycle of real-time information systems must be related to the objectives of the decision maker and determined in the context of specific decision-making needs. Thus, the decision maker's objectives in each instance are key factors in the design of effective information systems.

One reason why the use of fast-response information systems—even where they would be meaningful and useful—has been limited in the past, despite general business awareness of their existence and their benefits, is that they were thought to be too costly. As a matter of fact, the significant new departures in management information systems based on real time lie not so much in the improvement of actual data but in the design of systems that will use such data more effectively.

The importance of the time factor in an information system can range from almost negligible to crucial. The higher the dependence of the system on the time factor, the greater the need for developing fast-response systems. In the cases of high dependence, the event-data-time-action chain must be closely followed by the information-processing devices, and the time characteristics of transactions must be noted as they occur. In the past, effective real-time business information systems have been mostly restricted to such areas as sales order processing, finished goods inventory, and accounts receivable. However, real-time applications are now being expanded through the development of decision-making systems that require fast, tightly knit data-handling methods. Good data utilization can thus be tied to the basic requirements of the decision maker. For example, recent computer and communication design innovations permit events to be aggregated as they are recorded. Statistical algorithms can then provide continuous forecasting of future sets of events based on immediate past experience. These result-oriented forecasts are used to keep decision makers informed of current changes in the environment and of the implications of those changes to the business. The proper recognition and manipulation of time as a key variable in new management information systems is a major departure that can significantly increase management's ability to make effective decisions.

The control of highly seasonal style-goods retail inventories is a familiar example of the extent to which effective decision making is dependent on control of the time characteristics of input data. Seasonal factors and historical style life cycles characteristic of the specific communities, stores, departments, and price lines are all taken into account, and current information regarding sales of individual items is used to forecast future buying opportunities or markdown problems. A departmental inventory comprises a set of styles distributed by units that can differ in color, size, and quantity. Effective decisions regarding the number of styles to carry, the initial order quantity of new styles, reorder timing and quantity, and the amount of markdowns, all depend on events (sale of specific style, color, size) that occur during the seasonal cycle.[6]

In a style merchandising decision model, data such as historical performance and current economic indicators are subjected to a series of analyses performed through algorithms. Current information is thus assimilated and prepared to inform the decision maker of the likely consequences of new decisions. The rate of customer acceptance of a style is the key decision parameter. Knowledge of the timing of this rate and of how it can be used to make effective decisions has been shown to provide competitive advantages and significantly improved operating results. The style merchandising model allows the decision maker to decide more promptly and effectively—at any time—whether to do nothing about a style, reorder it, or mark it down. By permitting decisions on an average of one day earlier per style than did previous information systems, the new systems have been shown to increase a price line's profitability by 30 to 100 percent. That was when decisions resulting from both systems were the same. Considering that better decisions result from better forecasts, even better results are possible with the new system.

Similar decision systems based on real-time requirements, and the information necessary to back them up, are within the grasp of all executives today.

SIMULATION SYSTEMS

In contrast to step-by-step, real-time decision processes are decisions affecting events that will take place far in the future. For example, compare a retail store's decision to purchase a style item that will sell within a few days or not at all with an investment decision whose payouts will not come for many years. Although the time dependency of such decisions is clear, the relationship of

[6] See P. G. Carlson, "Managing Style Goods Inventories," *Stores Magazine*, June, 1961.

that dependency to information at hand is highly uncertain. Also, for longer-range processes the number of variables and parameters grows. In the future, each variable will take on some of a wide possible range of specific values that the decision maker cannot now know. The variables are interrelated and interlocked. Once decisions are made and resources are committed, many connected events will combine to determine the actual outcome. Hopefully, these events will be reasonably close to what was expected when the critical actions were taken.

New departures in management information systems introduce approaches that attempt to maximize management's understanding and ability to deal with uncertainty about the future. By using management science techniques and the power of the computer to take into account all available relevant information, these approaches describe the outcome of different courses of action in terms of a range of possible returns and measure the chances of the occurrence of each return in this range. The weighing of each of the possible returns with the chances for its occurrence helps management estimate which are the probable outcomes. Since there will be a set of undesirable outcomes in any range, the probable occurrence of undesirable outcomes is also estimated. Thus, by informing management of the likelihood and possible extent of future dangers, the new management information systems can now answer key questions for long-range corporate planning.

In investment decisions, resources are committed to achieve anticipated results. The actual future outcomes depend on many factors that will mature in a future competitive environment whose characteristics can only be estimated. Each of the many factors that should be considered in evaluating a specific commitment is subject to uncertainty. To determine the future environment in which an investment can come to fruition, an executive needs a picture of the effects of the uncertainty surrounding each significant factor. As indicated in the previous chapter, simulation systems will help provide such a picture.

Simulation of the way factors may combine in the future is a key to extracting the maximum amount of information from available forecasts and estimates. Simulation is like the process the executive must go through in his own mind when he finally makes a decision: weighing the pros and cons, summing up the chances that one set of events will occur rather than another, and, finally, arriving at a conclusion as to whether a given alternative is desirable. Simulation merely makes this process explicit and imposes a discipline on the planning and information procedure that increases the value, many times over, of what is already known and developed within a firm.

The development of such a simulation model for overall corporate operations, for example, requires estimates of such factors as market size, market share, selling prices, market growth rate, investments, and operating costs. An information system of this kind for management would require the following steps:

1. Estimating the range of uncertainty attached to each factor and the frequencies of the possible values the factor may attain

2. Deciding how the factors may be combined to provide a measure of return on a particular alternative

3. Selecting a set of values for each of these factors, chosen at random from the frequency distributions of the possible values

4. Computing the rate of return from that particular combination of factor values

5. Repeating the process of selection and computation often enough to define and evaluate rigorously the odds on the occurrence of each outcome

The new departure in this process is that a listing of all possible rates of return, ranging from a loss (if current factors combine unfavorably) to maximum possible gains, is now available to management. The likelihood of occurrence is determined for each of these values.

Although the development of simulation models is a straightforward matter, it has many subtle and important implications. The sensitivity, for example, of the final result to one or more uncertain factors is directly determinable, and this is significant. The most important input factors for resource allocation and investment decisions are undoubtedly uncertain. Yet previously available means of handling this kind of information have tended to mask the effects of this uncertainty. In other words, this kind of model is meaningful because it enables management to obtain and use all available data in a logical and powerful way, to use this knowledge to analyze the uncertainty of factors affecting final results, and to determine the risk and expected return of alternative decisions.

"OPTIMIZATION" SYSTEMS

The establishment of policies under which an enterprise operates is a primary function of management. Therefore, to provide guidelines for the formulation of decision rules for more effective operations, enlightened executives are constantly reviewing the impact of policies on operating results. Information systems based on management science models now give the executive a firm foundation for preparing and evaluating alternative policies and strategies. How do these models operate?

Deciding on policies requires the selection of objectives and programs and also of rules and guidelines for modification or control of environmental and input factors and variables. In general, management tries to select policies that will optimize some combination of its objectives. (It is, of course, by now clearly understood that no such thing as overall "optimization" is possible. We are always "suboptimizing"; that is, there are always things we do *not* control that lead us to do only the "best under the circumstances.") As indicated above, the formal models and simulations now available can, within certain limits, describe outcomes of alternative choices within a policy framework, and they can indicate what combinations of variables will provide optimum results. Thus, they represent a radical departure from past information systems. As we have seen, such models specify the various interrelated and interlocked factors that influence profit or other objectives and the sensitivity of the output to changes in the various inputs.

For example, Figure 3-1 illustrates the cost categories of a product-distribution system and the main policy areas [7] affecting those costs, along with the key operational characteristics of the system. An analysis will show that the policies do not always affect the costs directly; often they affect costs indirectly, through intermediate variables (operational characteristics) of order frequency, order size, demand volume, demand mix, and demand location. Decisions on policies in the nineteen areas listed can be greatly improved by new management information systems using models that price out and "optimize" the effects of changes in a specific policy (such as warehouse location or mode of transportation) on

[7] Of course, the list of policy areas is not necessarily exhaustive.

Cost and Policy Analysis of a Distribution System

POLICIES AFFECT KEY OPERATIONAL CHARACTERISTICS, WHICH IN TURN AFFECT COSTS. SIGNIFICANT RELATIONSHIPS OF POLICIES AND CHARACTERISTICS TO COSTS ARE INDICATED BY "X."

POLICY AREAS	COST CATEGORIES				
	CUSTOMER FREIGHT	INTERPLANT FREIGHT	TRAFFIC SERVICES	WAREHOUSING AND SHIPPING	SALES ORDER SERVICES AND MANAGEMENT
1. Quantity discounts	X		X	X	X
2. Direct sale to retailers	X		X	X	X
3. Specific shipment days	X			X	
4. Drop shipments	X		X	X	X
5. Delivery-cycle standards	X	X	X	X	X
6. Minimum order sizes	X		X	X	X
7. Optimum case sizes	X			X	
8. Back orders	X		X	X	X
9. Returned goods	X			X	
10. Deals	X			X	
11. Product-line pruning	X	X		X	
12. Make-or-buy	X	X			
13. Service area designation	X	X		X	
14. Assignment of manufacturing sources		X		X	
15. Sources of supply		X		X	
16. Shipment to a customer from one warehouse only	X	X		X	
17. New warehouses	X	X		X	
18. New manufacturing locations	X	X		X	
19. Company-owned transportation	X	X			

KEY OPERATIONAL CHARACTERISTICS

	CUSTOMER FREIGHT	INTERPLANT FREIGHT	TRAFFIC SERVICES	WAREHOUSING AND SHIPPING	SALES ORDER SERVICES AND MANAGEMENT
1. Order frequency	X		X	X	X
2. Order size	X			X	
3. Demand volume	X	X	X	X	X
4. Demand mix	X	X		X	X
5. Demand location	X	X		X	

FIGURE 3-1

the variables that directly influence cost. The models are formal descriptions of the movement of products (for example, through a production and distribution network) and algorithms (such as linear programming) that describe relevant interactions and costs. Such management information systems can be designed to develop an accurate representation of a total system so that the cost and revenue effects of alternative policies can be determined.

The key result is the development of a formal model with the capacity to produce a relevant description of the total distribution system and to capture, store, and retrieve as required the detailed data needed to evaluate alternatives. The computerized retention of detailed geographical, chronological, and demographical inter-action information has been a significant step in this revolutionary approach to policy decisions. This information has provided a basis for the use of formal models for short- and long-term forecasting and for the development of distribution, activity sequencing, resource acquisition, resource allocation, and overall control policies.

Far from being simply a formal mathematical exercise in optimization, a model allows the executive to examine a wide range of alternatives in a flexible way and to determine the feasibility, consistency, cost effectiveness, and profitability of various possible policies. The development of this model required (as do most such models):

1. Formulation of an algebraic or arithmetic representation of the system affected by the policy or policies under consideration. This requires analysis of the factors that describe the system (in terms of independent external variables and combinations of internal variables that can be used to represent actual interactions and flows through the system from product source to ultimate consumer). Ultimately, this analysis permits the description of the system to be written as a series of equations involving the variables.

2. Determination of the detailed relationships of the variables in the equations. This implies the ability to obtain, store, and properly sort detailed information. Fortunately, this can now be done without the tons of paper and man-years of clerical work that would have been required not very long ago. (Otherwise such systems would be mere academic exercises.)

3. Determination of the costs of products and of the capacities and costs of warehousing and distribution facilities associated with

the production of items and their movement through the system from product source to customer.

IMPLEMENTING THE MODERN INFORMATION SYSTEM

The wealth of models described in management science literature and the concurrently developed computer systems for efficient handling of internal data can now provide management with key decision-making information on a timely and accurate basis. However, many executives have missed the vital point of this new departure in information systems: *the collection and storage of masses of data is virtually meaningless without the concurrent development and use of effective models for determining likely cost and revenue consequences of alternative courses of action.*

The key significance of these new departures in management information systems is that they provide *action information*. This information is distinguished from mere data, accounting or cost descriptions, or so-called control or exception reports, because it pinpoints action implications. All of these models analyze the probable effects of alternative courses of action. The more accurately they do this, the greater will be management's ability to make effective decisions.

The mathematical models and supporting hardware that underlie the simulation and optimization techniques are now available at reasonable cost. The chief implementation problem is to educate managers to appreciate and understand the benefits and limitations of being able to analyze alternative courses of action. If the analytical approach is to be used successfully, the management team (and not simply a single executive) must understand it and apply it to broad areas of decision making. In fact, the management team itself must be deeply involved in the analysis of its own decision process. This is not easy. The tendency is to shy away from real penetration into ongoing decisions and to argue either that such decisions are too complicated or that significant alternatives are not available. But neither of these arguments is valid in light of the successful applications of the approach by diverse groups in government and by large and small businesses.

The necessary involvement of management also emphasizes a

Information System Structure

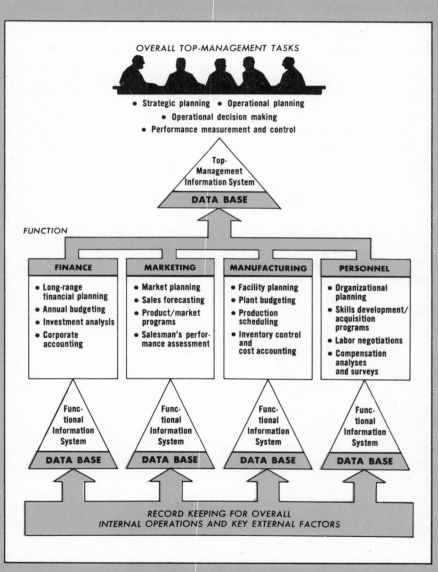

OVERALL TOP-MANAGEMENT TASKS

- Strategic planning   • Operational planning
- Operational decision making
- Performance measurement and control

Top-Management Information System

DATA BASE

FUNCTION

FINANCE	MARKETING	MANUFACTURING	PERSONNEL
• Long-range financial planning • Annual budgeting • Investment analysis • Corporate accounting	• Market planning • Sales forecasting • Product/market programs • Salesman's performance assessment	• Facility planning • Plant budgeting • Production scheduling • Inventory control and cost accounting	• Organizational planning • Skills development/acquisition programs • Labor negotiations • Compensation analyses and surveys

Functional Information System

DATA BASE

Functional Information System

DATA BASE

Functional Information System

DATA BASE

Functional Information System

DATA BASE

RECORD KEEPING FOR OVERALL INTERNAL OPERATIONS AND KEY EXTERNAL FACTORS

FIGURE 3-2

great danger inherent in attempts to use analytical sy
Formal techniques of handling information or measuring
quences of alternatives can lead only to unfortunate results
plied by executives who lack a deep understanding of the underlying economics of their business. Those who help management help
itself in applying these new systems must also understand the
organizational implications of replacing a compartmentalized
approach with an efficient, timely, overall information flow. If
applications are to be effective, the business must be viewed as a
system, not just as a set of vaguely integrated and coordinated
functions. As Figure 3-2 indicates, the basic information systems
for each key business function (finance, marketing, manufacturing, personnel) must be tied into a top-management system that
permits optimal planning and decision making at the top to be
related to optimal decision making in each function—all systems
resting on the fundamental record-keeping data base.

Regardless of the difficulty of applying these new systems, today's competitive environment forces the executive to strive to
make better decisions and to formulate better policies. Whenever
competition begins to use better decision-making methods for such
functions as forecasting, scheduling, allocation, or pricing, the
firms falling behind in the use of these methods will lose increasing
amounts of competitive ground. For example, more and more
companies have had to develop an interest in control reports on
previously neglected aspects of customer service: promises-kept reports, delivery-cycle reports, back-order analyses, and so forth. But
simply keeping this information is useless unless the effect and cost
of changing the inputs are clear.

New departures are being made every day. The language that
management speaks is changing, and the transactions and other
events in a business have undergone radical alteration in just a
short time. As we have seen, management will always be faced with
the problem of making choices. These choices simply will be trans-
ferred to a higher level than ever before, since the deeper the understanding, the more meaning can be inferred from a given
decision-making situation. And the use of these new systems will
influence the environment because only the better systems survive.
In the long run, their use will be vital to the survival of any business or organization.

CHAPTER *4*

Planning Long-range Business Strategy

M*ANY* businessmen are yet unaware of how effectively management science can clarify difficult and complex policy decisions. Models can be developed today that spell out, far more sharply and usefully than was ever possible before, the potential risks and returns on investment involving thousands or millions of dollars. As a result, losses may be avoided and profit opportunities improved. The use of these models—tailored to specific business problems—was not practical until the same techniques that scientists have used so effectively on physical phenomena were used to analyze business.

The usefulness of management science techniques for major business policy or strategy decisions stems from the use of the systems (model-building) approach to problems of complexity and uncertainty. As we have seen, computers make the approach more attractive. Thousands upon thousands of companies—30,000 today, by one estimate—have computers, but far fewer companies have taken significant advantage of new management science methods. Thus, these methods offer the alert executive an opportunity to achieve real competitive advantages for his company.

PLANNING FOR DECISION MAKING

An actual example can best show how effectively management science is helping executives reach major, long-range corporate strategy decisions. The top management of a large company—a producer, processor, and marketer of a commodity-type product—recently faced the following situation.

Every year, the company's overseas mills produced over a million tons of raw material for shipment to the continental United States. About 75 percent of the raw material went to the company's West Coast plant, where it was made into more than forty consumer and industrial products for sale nationwide. The remaining 25 percent was shipped through the Panama Canal to be sold as a raw product to processors in the Gulf States region or on the New York open market.

Business had been satisfactorily profitable for many years, but now changes were under way in the industry. Competitors had recently built a number of new plants and had stepped up plant improvements and mergers, with a resulting increase in shipments of competing products into the company's largest markets in the West and Midwest. Meanwhile, prices for the company's raw material on the open market had been rising, while prices for its finished products were remaining relatively stable.

On top of all this, the West Coast plant would soon be operating at full capacity and would then require an investment of between $15 million and $25 million to meet the increasing demand for finished products. Meanwhile, however, two attractive alternative locations for a new plant had come to light, and it was possible that the company would benefit more in the long run by building new plants on one or both of those sites than by expanding the original plant.

In light of this situation, the Board of Directors asked the company's chief executive officer to develop answers to these questions:

First, with our good position in the raw material market, and with raw material prices rising, should we even try to compete in the processing-marketing business 5 to 10 years from now?

Second, if we should decide to compete, what will it be worth in dollars and cents to:

1. Expand our present plant, build new plants, or do both
2. Continue with our present markets or enter new ones
3. Continue to market our present mix of products or bring out a new line?

Further, should we use long-term debt financing?

Obviously, these were complex questions. Just as obviously, they raised basic issues of business strategy—issues such as any top management inevitably confronts from time to time.

What is business strategic planning, as this company carried it out? Business strategic planning is "top-down," long-range corporate planning that challenges the basic goals and directions that have guided the enterprise in the past. More technically stated, it should be *prospective* decision making, done after the systematic evaluation of all reasonable alternative courses of action and under whatever conditions of uncertainty exist in the long-term economic environment.

To illustrate, the executives of the company just described had to evaluate the practical courses of action systematically and then decide among them. Some of these were: expanding their existing plant, building new plants, entering new markets, and/or changing the product line. Overshadowing their decision making was their uncertainty about what competition would do in the future, what prices might be, and, of course, what nationwide economic events—such as recessions or special legislation unfavorable to their business—might occur to change the picture.

Strategic planning, as they carried it out, is an ongoing process. It should produce a "portfolio" of goals and plans—goals and plans which, though tailored to specific events (favorable or otherwise) that may occur in the future, can be *readily* reanalyzed and updated.

How, then, did these executives solve the strategic planning problem posed by the Board of Directors' questions? With available technology in the management sciences and computer systems, they could not attack the problem in the most straightforward way possible, which would have been to evaluate *all* possible alternatives and combinations of alternatives with various future possible economic conditions. There were too many alternatives even for the largest computers to handle.[1] However, they were able to develop the critical information on which to base their strategic plans. First, they selected the best corporate course of action from the alternatives within the most probable economic environment (the one they felt was most likely to occur). Second, they tested the impact of other, less probable environments upon these results and modified the initially selected course of action to minimize threats or to capitalize fully on opportunities. Third, they produced a portfolio of goals and plans that would enable them to react quickly to the real future environment as it unfolded.

As we have seen, the major components of their strategic planning problem were:

1. An uncertain future economic environment
2. Alternative corporate courses of action

Accordingly, to solve the strategic planning problem, they first had to define the likely future environments and specify reasonable corporate alternatives.

To define future economic environments that would have the greatest impact on corporate strategy, the company first had to identify the critical factors for this particular strategic problem and then had to decide how many values for each factor should be taken into consideration in planning. After analyzing the situation, this company's management concluded that the following four factors—in key market areas—at the levels indicated were critical:

- Population growth—low, expected, high
- Impact of substitute—expected and high
- Product prices—low, expected, and high
- Competition—expected and high

Note that with just these four factors and their various values, thirty-six different combinations of environments could be gener-

---

[1] This picture is, of course, continuously changing. The number of alternatives that can be examined economically with an appropriate programming algorithm and computer system continues to increase each year. The upper limit is not yet in sight.

ated $(3 \times 2 \times 3 \times 2)$. For example, one such environment would consist of (1) high population growth; (2) expected impact of substitute; (3) low product price; and (4) high competition.

After reviewing each of these thirty-six combinations, management selected eight as being the most important to test. These environments were:

■ A most probable environment—consisting of all factors at their "expected" values

■ Six less probable environments, each with one of the following factors at the values indicated (and the rest at the "expected" level)

—A low population
—A high population
—A low price
—A high price
—A high substitute impact
—A high level of competition

■ A most pessimistic environment—consisting of all factors at their most unfavorable values

By selecting these eight key environments to test, management was not simply discarding other combinations. Rather, it was focusing initially on those environments that (1) could reasonably be expected to occur and (2) would significantly affect the company's operations and hence the decisions that would have to be made in advance.

Having defined eight key future economic environments, management next had to specify the reasonable alternative corporate courses of action to be tested within each.

In the kinds of analyses described here, corporate courses of action can be divided into two broad categories: financial and operating. In this example, management had two financial alternatives: using long-term debt or continuing to finance the company's operations out of earnings and short-term borrowings.

Operating alternatives fall into two subcategories: manufacturing alternatives and marketing alternatives. In manufacturing, this company faced a fairly complex array of operating alternatives —eight in all:

1. To maintain the present West Coast plant capacity, or to expand it, in combination with the alternatives

2. To build no new plants or to build
   —A new large plant at location A
   —A new large plant at location B
   —Small plants at both locations

Analysis of these alternatives showed the eight combinations to be reasonable (one combination, for example, was not to expand the existing plant but to build a new large plant at location B). The company's marketing alternatives were:

1. To stay in the existing markets, or to enter new markets
2. To change or not to change the product line

Here there are four possible combinations (one combination, then, was staying in existing markets with the existing product line, while another was entering new markets with a new product line).

In total, then, the executives had sixty-four seemingly reasonable combinations of corporate courses of action—*two* financial alternatives times *eight* operating alternatives times *four* marketing alternatives—the consequences of which had to be sorted out. These were shortly to be combined with the selected economic environments, thus increasing significantly the magnitude of the problem that top management faced in systematically evaluating these combinations to develop a meaningful set of goals and plans for the future.

The total number of combinations (formed by the number of economic environments times the number of financial alternatives times operating-manufacturing alternatives times operating-marketing alternatives) virtually exploded. The grand total was 512 combinations for investigation—made up of eight environments times two financial alternatives times eight production alternatives times four marketing alternatives.

PROBLEM SOLVING

At this stage of the analysis, it would have been, of course, physically possible to evaluate each combination with nothing more than pencil, paper, and desk calculators. How long it would have taken is a matter for conjecture, in terms of detail, accuracy, and ease of rerunning. Thus, the computer, along with a management science model and algorithm, provided a method that initially eliminated as many nonsignificant alternatives as possible. This approach helped to cut the problem down to size by concentrating first on finding the best course of action within the "most probable" environment, and then testing this selection in the other seven less probable environments. The process was carried out in three phases:

Phase 1: After defining probable environments and identifying key corporate alternatives, a "base case" was run with:

- Most probable environment
- No changes in corporate operations or structure

The base case provided the basis for comparison in analyzing alternatives.

Phase 2: The objective in this phase was to reduce the number of alternatives. For the "most probable" environment, the company evaluated each of the sixty-four alternative courses of action and compared it to the base case, using return-on-investment criteria (other criteria could, of course, be used where appropriate). On the basis of these analyses, the most desirable course of action within the most probable environment was selected.

Phase 3: In this step, the impacts of other, less probable environments on the selected course of action were evaluated. In addition, one or more alternative courses of action previously eliminated were reevaluated where judgmental analysis indicated that they might prove more desirable in one of the less probable environments. The final output of this process was an updated portfolio of goals and plans covering all the selected environments.

Even though this approach kept down the number of combinations that required analysis, the company actually evaluated one base case, sixty-three alternatives within the probable environment, and three alternatives (the selected one plus two variations) for each of the remaining seven environments: eighty-five cases in all. Although significantly less than the 512 possible combinations, this number is still sizable by conventional standards. The key analytical tool in evaluating these combinations was what may be called a "strategic planning computer model."

The model used by this company is fairly typical of those used for analyzing major strategic decision problems. It was made up of three submodels—an environment model, a decision model, and a financial model—as follows:

Environment model: This model was used to generate the prices, demands, and costs associated with a selected environment. An environment model can be either "deterministic" (in which all input factors are given only a single value) or "probabilistic" (in which each significant factor is assigned a probability distribution describing the range of values that it can assume). We will see more of probabilistic models in the future. The model used by the company was deterministic but, as we have seen, was applied to a large number of different environments, and thus used some of the probabilistic information available.

Decision model: This model was used to "optimize" (on the basis of selected profit or return-on-investment criteria) the plant and operating configuration and levels of activity (production, inventories, modes of distribution, for example) for a designated environment.

Financial model: This model was used to produce *pro forma* income statements and balance sheets reflecting the financial results of selecting a particular course of action within a particular environment.

The three submodels in the strategic planning model can be further understood in terms of their functions and required input data. The primary function of this company's *environment model* was to compute the potential demand for each product group in each market, to adjust prices and costs for future inflation, and to compute product contribution margins for a particular environment. A series of equations was written to describe these calculations and then programmed for the computer. This submodel's input data consisted of the important environmental factors: for example, population, per capita consumption, and competitors' regional distributions. Additional input data for the environment model were the estimated maximum market shares and product mixes by market.

Once an environment had been selected, the *decision model* (in this case using linear programming) determined the levels of production and inventories, methods of distribution, and raw material sales that would maximize profits in the selected environment. In addition, the decision model identified those operating or policy constraints that were limitations on the company's ability to make additional profits in that environment—e.g., plant capacity. It also provided the potential dollar "opportunity value" [2] of relieving these binding constraints. Such information is extremely valuable in strategic planning and is a normal by-product of a linear programming model.

Input data for the decision model from the environment model included the potential demands for each product and the product contribution margin by market. In addition, the operating capacities and costs of the various plants and machines were required. Here, for example, management provided a range of operating capacities, costs, and investment requirements and let the decision model indicate which investments in capacity should or should not be made, according to their profitability.

Finally, the *financial model* used the output of the decision model to produce contribution margin reports by market and *pro forma* corporate income statements and also to perform discounted cash flow return-on-investment analysis of all new investments made in the case run. For input data, the financial model used the optimum allocations and the operating costs determined by the decision model and other income and expense data, such as depreciation schedules and fixed costs.

Each of these models produced computer printouts to describe the environment being tested, the optimum allocation, and the financial results. Most important from management's point of view were the *pro forma* financial statements, which enabled them to get a clear picture in ordinary, day-to-day terms of what the future *might* look like if they should take certain specific decisions under various economic forecasts.

One end result of this strategic planning process was a catalog of corporate courses of action according to their financial attractiveness in the environments tested, together with a time scale indicating deadlines by which decisions would have to be made. Figure 4-1 gives a simplified example of these results.

As Figure 4-1 shows, the company had a list of the major courses of action it could choose and a table summarizing the financial attractiveness [3] of each course of action in each of four tested environments. These indicated, first, that the company should re-

---

[2] Also called "shadow price" or "opportunity cost."

[3] The actual outputs were, as indicated, detailed financial statements in each case.

Testing Courses of Action

COURSE OF ACTION	ENVIRONMENTS F = Favorable outcome U = Unfavorable outcome				DECISION DEADLINE
	MOST PROB- ABLE	HIGH POP- ULATION	LOW PRICE	HIGH COM- PETITION	
STAY IN PROCESSING/ MARKETING	F	F	F	F	NONE
USE DEBT	F	F	F	F	NONE
NEW PLANT — A	F	F	F	F	Jan. 1970
NEW PLANT — B	U	U	U	U	NONE
EXPAND PLANT	F	F	F	U	Mar. 1969
NEW PRODUCT LINE	F	F	U	U	NOW
NEW MARKETS	U	U	U	U	NONE

FIGURE 4-1

main in the processing-marketing business and use, within reason, long-term debt financing in all environments.

Building a new plant only at location A turned out to be desirable in all environments. Expanding the existing plant was desirable in all environments but one. The new product line was a "go" in two environments but not in the other two, and entering new markets was not desirable in any environment.

Where a course of action—for example, a new product line for this company—would be desirable in some environments but not in others, and a decision must be made now, before the new environment can be known, the top management must, in making a final decision, assess the risk involved: i.e., the probability of a favorable future environment and the size of the stake. As will shortly be seen in some detail, management science can help him analyze this risk.

It should be noted that the management science procedures and methods that this company used to help plan long-range business strategy could be equally well applied to other strategy planning in that company or, indeed, in almost any other company. Taken together, these procedures and methods constitute a new and powerful kind of general-purpose tool, the *quantitative model for long-range strategy planning*. The rest of this chapter describes other management science tools for planning.

RISK ANALYSIS

Figure 4-1 showed that management could have made no single decision regarding new product lines that would have been best for all possible future environments. If competition had remained unchanged, the company would have profited by introducing new products; if competition had become considerably more severe, the company would have been better off not introducing new products. (Briefly, this was because greater competition would have significantly reduced profits on new finished products, while the company could have been reasonably sure of comfortable profit margins on increased sales of raw products.) Yet, as the decision date indicated, management had to make a decision by that time, despite uncertainty about the future environment. An approach called *risk analysis* can be useful in a situation where the outcome depends on uncertain environmental conditions.

The management of this company agreed that it would be unwise to simply choose the most likely environment and assume that it was going to come about. It was also clear that in such a situation knowledge about the nature of the uncertainty of the various environments and about the size of the stake involved could affect the decision maker's choice. In fact, this is precisely what is meant by risk. Risk is dependent on both the amount of uncertainty and the size of the stake involved.

How the two factors influence decisions might be illustrated by asking the reader to play a game—or rather, asking him to choose which of two games he would like to play. One plays the game he chooses just once. A coin is to be flipped once in each game; it is a fair, unbiased coin.

In game A, if the coin comes up heads, the player will get 5 cents; if the coin comes up tails, he will get 5 cents. That is, 5 cents is a sure thing. In game B, on the other hand, if the coin comes up heads, he will get 15 cents; if the coin comes up tails, he will get nothing.

Now, would you pick game A or game B? Game B, in all likelihood. The reason is perhaps obvious; the long-run average, the best-guess outcome, the "expected value" of game B is, in this situation, 7½ cents—a 50-50 chance of winning 15 cents. And the equivalent stake of 5 cents is negligible (the 5 cents is a stake because not to choose A risks losing a sure return).

Let us change the stakes a little without changing the rules. In game A, the player will get $50 regardless of whether the coin comes up heads or tails. In game B, on the other hand, if the coin comes up heads, he will get $150; if the coin comes up tails, he will get nothing. He would probably still prefer game B, for the $50 stake is perhaps minor compared to a 50-50 chance for $150.

Let us try once more. In game A, $5 million is a sure thing. Game B offers a 50-50 chance at $15 million. This time, almost anyone would prefer game A. And yet game B still has the greater "expected value"—$7.5 million.

This shows how information about uncertainty and the size of the stake affects personal and business decisions. If, in this game example, the only information available was the expected value of each of the games, a player would have had no rational alternative but to choose game B in all three cases, since it has the higher expected value. However, knowing that game B involved a substantial amount of uncertainty, whereas game A did not, one would very likely have chosen game A in particular circumstances. Further, this game example showed that either the size of the stake or the amount at risk can affect the player's decision, even though nothing else might change. When the size of the stake got high enough—in this case, $5 million—most of us chose to follow a more conservative course of action. In other words, information on the amount risked causes a person to make a different decision.

It should be pointed out that a "best-guess" analysis—that is, an analysis using only the most likely value for each of the various key factors—would totally conceal the uncertainty information that would lead one to make different decisions regarding the games. Companies have always used best-guess analysis in investment decisions. By contrast, the management science approach known as risk analysis (which was briefly discussed in Chapter 3 in the section on simulation systems) makes it possible for management to have and use this uncertainty information. Risk analysis permits the manager to know more accurately the degree of risk that he is incurring by choosing a given course of action. Further, as will be seen, risk analysis may actually help the manager reduce this risk by indicating to him which among the factors that he *can* influence contributes to it most significantly. An example of an actual case in which risk analysis was used to analyze a new-product venture will clarify these points.

A company in the foods field was considering putting a new candy on the market. There were eight key environmental factors bearing on the decision (Figure 4-2). As is characteristic of new-product ventures, all were highly uncertain. Information on the range of uncertainties associated with each of these factors was gathered and a probability distribution [4] was determined for each. For example, Figure 4-3 depicts the resulting probability distribution of the total market size for the first year after the introduction of the new product.

The probability distributions of all eight key factors were then inserted into the risk analysis model, a simulation model like those described previously. The results of the risk analysis showed the range of possible financial outcomes that could be expected from carrying out this new-product venture as initially planned, and the

[4] The chances or probabilities associated with each possible event (or events) being described by the range of uncertainties.

Environmental Factors Determining Return on Investment in Confectionery Business

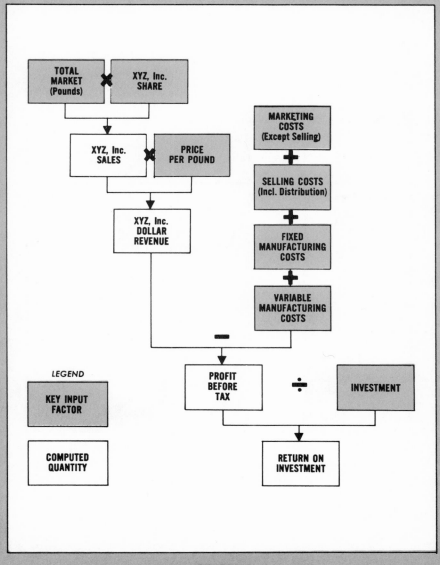

FIGURE 4-2

Probability Distribution of Total Market Size

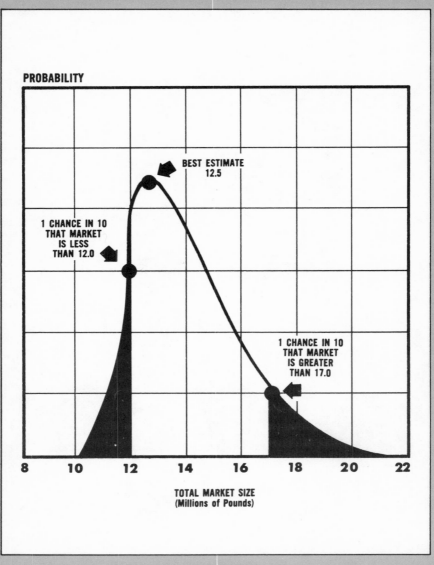

PROBABILITY

BEST ESTIMATE
12.5

1 CHANCE IN 10
THAT MARKET
IS LESS
THAN 12.0

1 CHANCE IN 10
THAT MARKET
IS GREATER
THAN 17.0

8   10   12   14   16   18   20   22

TOTAL MARKET SIZE
(Millions of Pounds)

FIGURE 4-3

Overall Return on Investment From Confectionery Business

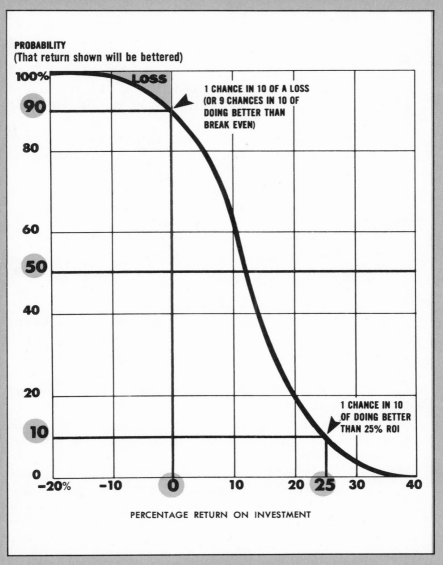

PROBABILITY
(That return shown will be bettered)

LOSS

1 CHANCE IN 10 OF A LOSS
(OR 9 CHANCES IN 10 OF
DOING BETTER THAN
BREAK EVEN)

1 CHANCE IN 10
OF DOING BETTER
THAN 25% ROI

PERCENTAGE RETURN ON INVESTMENT

FIGURE 4-4

probabilities that each of various possible returns on investment would result.

As originally conceived, the proposed venture offered an expected return of approximately 14 percent after taxes. This would have been the only reasonable return about which management would have learned, had it been estimated by traditional methods. But the risk analysis method yielded the "risk profile" given in Figure 4-4, in which the 14 percent return appears at the point of 50 percent probability. Particularly vital further intelligence produced by risk analysis revealed that the venture stood a 1-in-10 chance of incurring a loss, and a less than 1-in-10 chance of achieving a 25 percent return. (These values are indicated also in the risk profile, Figure 4-4.)

Given *only* the information on the expected return of 14 percent —a satisfactory rate of return for this particular company— management would have accepted the proposed investment. However, given the additional information that there was a 10 percent chance of incurring a significant loss, management had serious second thoughts about accepting this proposal.

To facilitate its decision, management developed and analyzed an alternative way of entering this business. This involved a less fully integrated method of manufacturing the product and a different distribution channel. The results of a risk analysis of the second alternative are shown in Figure 4-5.

The expected return from this alternative is lower—11 percent —but there is almost no uncertainty involved. Although an 11 percent return to this company was a fairly acceptable rate, management still had a rather sticky decision to make. Should it accept the marginally attractive but highly certain 11 percent rate of return, or should it accept the 14 percent expected rate of return with a significant chance of achieving a much higher or lower rate of return? Risk analysis will not make this decision for the manager, but it will provide him with useful information upon which to base his decision, and it will help him decide how to use it. (This management took the conservative course—accepting the 11 percent; another management might have decided differently; but each would know *why* the decision was made.)

Sensitivity analysis is a technique used to identify those factors in a decision situation that have the greatest effect, or leverage, on

RISK PROFILE
Return on Investment From Confectionery Business

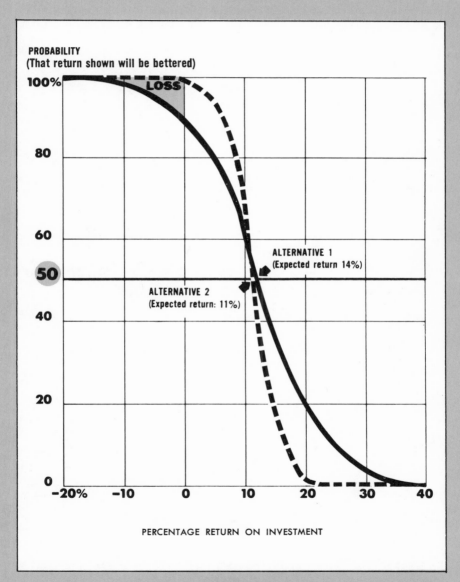

FIGURE 4-5

Uncertainty Profile
of Key Factors

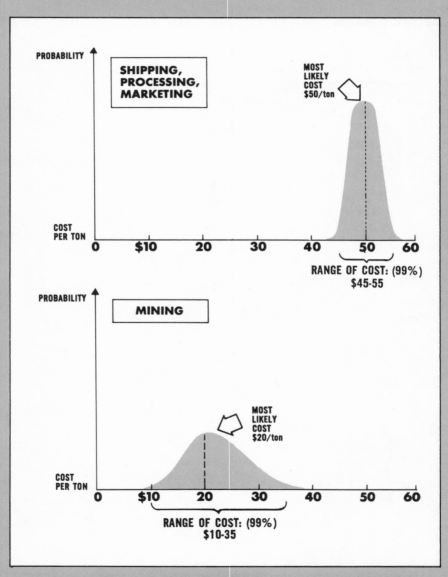

FIGURE 4-6

the outcome. Often, of course, a factor that has the largest numerical effect on the outcome is known with virtual certainty, while another factor that has a numerically smaller effect on the outcome is highly uncertain. For example, consider one company that was mining, shipping, processing, and marketing a mineral product. The shipping, processing, and marketing costs were known with virtual certainty, and the likelihood that their total would possibly go below $45 or above $55 per ton was considered to be slight. By contrast, the cost of bringing the material to the surface—that is, the mining cost—could be as low as $10 per ton if everything went right or as high as $35 if there should be unusually severe flooding, if the overburden should be more difficult to work with than expected, and if there were unusual labor difficulties. The best-guess estimate for the mining cost was $20 a ton —lower than for the known shipping, processing, and marketing costs, but so much less certain that it was by far the most significant factor to which management could direct its attention. The contrasting uncertainty profiles for the two types of cost are plotted in Figure 4-6.

Without the information on uncertainty and this method of sensitivity, which risk analysis made possible, the facts of the situation might not have been apparent to management. But, given this additional information, management could concentrate on reducing the mining cost, or at least attempting to reduce the range of uncertainty by getting better information (through research and exploration, among other things).

In summary, the risk analysis approach is useful for top-management decision making in situations where no one course of action is clearly most profitable and where considerable uncertainty is associated with the future environment and with the factors affecting the decision. Risk analysis provides management with specific information on the level of risk that it will incur in taking a particular course of action. And finally, because risk analysis can tell management which factors contribute most significantly to that risk, management may be able to influence those factors. These three results, in combination with those from other systematic analyses (such as linear programming models), should provide the basis for effective long-range strategy planning in today's complex and highly competitive markets.

CHAPTER 5

Capital Investment Analysis

O_F all the decisions that business executives must make, none is more insistent, challenging, and, of course, potentially rewarding than that of choosing among alternative capital investment opportunities. Once the opportunities have been identified, it is not difficult to project the impact of the investment on future profits and returns under various assumptions about the future. The difficulty lies in deciding on the validity of the assumptions about such factors as sales, costs, and market share, and their implications. Each assumption involves a certain degree—often a high degree—of uncertainty. Taken together, these uncertainties can multiply into a total uncertainty which, when combined with the investment stake, often introduces a risk of critical proportions. It is in the evaluation of risk that the executive has been able to get little help from older tools and techniques.

As suggested in preceding chapters, risk analysis now offers the executive a realistic means of measuring the risks involved in capital investment decisions. Armed with this measurement, which evaluates for him the odds on each possible level of return, the executive is in a more knowledgeable position to weigh alternative courses of action against corporate objectives.

Risk analysis, then, is a management science technique for evaluating the uncertainties involved in alternative proposals for major capital investment. In this chapter we shall examine risk analysis in detail; in Chapter 6 we shall see how recent developments based on risk analysis can serve as guides to management in formulating company policies for combining proposed capital investments into a rational pattern to meet stated corporate objectives.

NEED FOR NEW CONCEPT

The evaluation of a capital investment project starts with the principle that the potential productivity of capital is measured by the return an investor may expect over some future period. A dollar received next year is worth less than a dollar in hand today, because one can presumably invest today's dollar at some rate of return and have more than a dollar in hand a year from now. For the same reason, expenditures to be made three years from now are less costly than the same expenditures would be two years hence. Thus, the rate of return cannot be calculated realistically unless one takes into account both (1) the time investment funds are to be expended and (2) the time investment returns are to be received.

Comparing alternative investments is therefore complicated by the fact that investments usually differ not only in cost and revenue but also in the length of time over which expenditures will have to be made and in the timing of the payouts.

These basic investment facts revealed long ago the shortcomings of approaches that measure the relative attractiveness of alternatives by (1) averaging and ratioing annual benefits and expenditures or (2) lumping annual benefits and expenditures—as does the number-of-years-to-pay-out method. These shortcomings have stimulated students of decision making to explore more precise methods of evaluating and ranking proposed investments. It is not surprising, therefore, that much effort has been devoted to developing ways to determine the values to a company of alternative capital investments. The accepted ways to calculate alternative capital investment values and to measure the rate of future return on an investment made today are discounted cash flow analysis and the closely related present worth analysis.[1]

Thus, these methods are more or less elaborate mathematical formulas for comparing the outcomes of various investments and the combinations of the variables that will affect the investments. As these techniques have been refined, the mathematical operations involved have become more and more precise—so precise that discounted returns can now be calculated to a fraction of a percentage point.

But the sophisticated businessman knows that these precise calculations are based on imprecise data. At best, the rate-of-return information that the businessman receives is an "average" based on different estimates with varying reliabilities and different ranges of probability. When the expected returns on two investments do not differ greatly, he is likely to be influenced by factors whose probable impact cannot be calculated. Even when the figures for two investments are so different that the choice seems clear, memories of the Edsel and other ill-fated "surefire" ventures lurk in the back of the businessman's mind.

In short, the decision maker realizes that there is something more he ought to know: something other than the expected rate of return. He suspects that the uncertainty is in the nature and processing of the data on which the expected rate of return is calculated. It has something to do with a wide range of possible and uncertain outcomes and probabilities of rewards and risks.

The Achilles heel

The fatal weakness of past attempts to compare capital investments thus has nothing to do with the mathematics of rate-of-

[1] In the discounted cash flow method the investment is analyzed as though it were a mortgage. From a discount table, a rate is selected that will discount the annual cash revenues less costs to a total present worth equal to the capital outlay. This rate is then the "discounted rate of return." In present worth analysis, on the other hand, a rate of return that the company feels it must earn is the starting point and the value of the investment is determined by discounting the proposed cash flows back to a present worth using this rate. For an extended general discussion of the application of these concepts, see "Eyeing the ROI," by Stanley B. Henrice, in the *Harvard Business Review*, May–June 1968, pp. 88–97.

return calculation. The fact is that, no matter what mathematical process is used, many of the variables entering into the calculation of rate of return are subject to significant levels of uncertainty.

For example, the useful life of a new piece of capital equipment is rarely known in advance. It may be affected by variations in obsolescence or deterioration, and relatively small changes in useful life can lead to large changes in return. Yet one specific value for the life of the equipment, based on a great deal of data from which a single best possible forecast has been developed, is entered into the rate-of-return calculation. The same is done for the other factors that have a significant bearing on the decision at hand.

Figure 5-1 shows how difficult it is to determine the nature of the actual risk faced, even for a simple project in which the sales costs and capital outlay are totaled over the life of the investment. Using reasonable ranges for each of the variables involved (e.g., a best guess of 200,000 units for sales volume, with a range from 175,000 to 225,000 units), the calculation shows that the outcome, in terms of average return on investment, may vary anywhere from zero to 56.5 percent! Thus, even an approach using ranges has a fatal weakness: if the actual outcome for any variable is significantly different from the estimate, the actual results of the investment may be *very* different from those projected, and there is no way of knowing what the chances are that any value in a given range will be achieved.[2]

This uncertainty is illustrated by a simple case, one in which the odds appear to be all in favor of a particular decision. The executives of a food company must decide whether or not to launch a new packaged cereal. They have concluded that there are five determining variables: advertising and promotion expense, total cereal marketing, share of market for the product, operating costs, and new capital investment. On the basis of the "most likely" estimate for each of these variables, the future looks bright: a healthy 30 percent return. This return, however, depends on realization of each of the most likely estimates. If each of these "educated guesses" has, for example, a 60 percent chance of being correct (which is rather good) there is only an 8 percent chance that *all five*

[2] Figure 5-2, using the familiar example of a pair of dice, shows how the odds on any given outcome for a throw of the pair can be determined by finding all the combinations that can occur. Thus, 6 sevens (out of 36) equals 1 in 6 chances of a seven; 1 two has 1 in 36 chances.

Analyses Based on Single Point and Range Estimates

$$\text{FORMULA: ROI} = \frac{(\text{PRICE X UNIT SALES}) - \text{COSTS}}{\text{INVESTMENT}}$$

LIKELY RANGE	LOW	HIGH
PRICE	$5.00	$5.50
UNIT SALES	175,000	225,000
COSTS	$700,000	$875,000
INVESTMENT	$950,000	$1,100,000

PESSIMISTIC CASE   **ROI**

$$\frac{(\$5 \text{ X } 175,000) - \$875,000}{\$1,100,000} = 0\%$$

BEST ESTIMATE CASE

$$\frac{(\$5 \text{ X } 200,000) - \$800,000}{\$1,000,000} = 20\%$$

OPTIMISTIC CASE

$$\frac{(\$5.50 \text{ X } 225,000) - \$700,000}{\$950,000} = 56.5\%$$

FIGURE 5-1

will be correct $(0.60 \times 0.60 \times 0.60 \times 0.60 \times 0.60)$! So the "expected" return is actually dependent on a rather unlikely coincidence. The decision maker needs to know a great deal more about the *other* values used to make each of the five estimates and about what he stands to gain or lose from various combinations of these values.

This simple example shows that the rate of return actually depends on a specific combination of values of a great many variables. But very often only the expected levels of ranges (e.g., worst, average, best; or pessimistic, most likely, optimistic) of these variables are used in calculating the figures given to management. As we have seen, projecting a single most likely rate of return or the worst, average, and best possibilities gives seemingly precise numbers; but these numbers do not tell the whole story, because the expected rate of return represents only a few points on a continuous curve of possible combinations of future happenings.

Using the expected rate in predicting the rate of return is a bit like trying to predict the outcome in a dice game by saying that the most likely outcome is a seven. The prediction is incomplete because it does not tell us about all the other things that could happen. Figure 5-2, for instance, shows the odds on throws of only two dice, each having six sides. Now, suppose that there are eight dice, each having 100 sides. This is a situation more comparable to business investment, where the company's market share might become any one of 100 different percentage points and where there are eight different factors (pricing, promotion, and so on) that can affect the outcome. Building up a "distribution" of the possible outcomes of throwing these eight dice would give management a much more realistic and comprehensive picture of the alternative, just as Figure 5-2 represents the distribution of possible outcomes in an ordinary dice game.

Nor is this the only trouble. Willingness to bet on a roll of the dice depends not only on the odds but also, as we have seen, on the stakes. Since the probability of rolling a seven is 1 in 6 throws, one might be quite willing to risk a few dollars on that outcome at odds, for example, of 10 to 1. But would one be equally willing to wager $10,000 or $100,000 at those same odds, or even at better odds? In short, risk is influenced both by the odds on the occurrence of various events and by the magnitude of the rewards or penalties that are involved when they do occur.

Describing Uncertainty

A THROW OF THE DICE
(ALL POSSIBLE OUTCOMES)

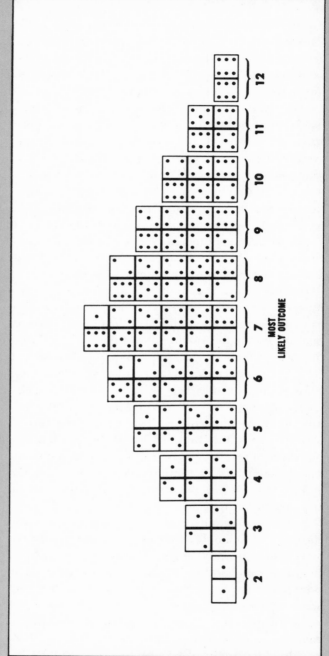

FIGURE 5-2

To illustrate again, suppose a company is considering an investment of $1 million. The "best" estimate of the projected annual net revenue is $200,000. Perhaps this estimate is the average of three possible returns: a 1-in-3 chance of getting *no return at all;* a 1-in-3 chance of getting *$200,000 per year;* and a 1-in-3 chance of getting *$400,000 per year.*[3] Suppose that getting no return at all would put the company out of business. Then, by accepting this proposal, management would be taking a 1-in-3 chance of going bankrupt.

However, if *only* the "best estimate" analysis were known, management might go ahead, unaware that it was taking a big chance. If all of the available information were examined, management might prefer an alternative proposal with a smaller, but more certain (i.e., less variable), expectation.

Such considerations have led almost all advocates of the use of modern capital-investment-index calculations to seek recognition of the role played by the elements of uncertainty.

How can the executive clear away uncertainties that surround each available choice among alternative decisions?

Limited improvements

A number of efforts to cope with uncertainty have been successful up to a point, but all seem to fall short of the mark in one way or another:

1. *More accurate forecasts.* Reducing the error in estimates is a worthy objective. But no matter how many estimates of the future go into a capital investment decision, the future is still the future when all is said and done. Therefore, no matter how well one fore-

---

[3] The estimate is worked out as follows:

Probability	Revenue	Probability × Revenue
1/3	0	0
1/3	$200,000	$\dfrac{\$200,000}{3}$
1/3	$400,000	$\dfrac{\$400,000}{3}$

$$\text{Expected (average) return}=0+\frac{\$200,000}{3}+\frac{\$400,000}{3}=\frac{\$600,000}{3}=\$200,000$$

Thus, expected return equals, as one would expect, the sum of the values of all possible outcomes weighted by the chances that each outcome may occur.

casts, one is still left with the certain knowledge that uncertainty cannot be entirely eliminated.

2. *Empirical adjustments.* Before-the-fact adjustment of or change in the factors influencing the outcome of a decision is subject to serious qualifications and difficulties. One would like to adjust them so as to cut down the likelihood of a "bad" investment, but how can this be done without at the same time spoiling the chance to make a "good" investment? And in any case, what is the basis for adjustment? One adjusts for bias, not for uncertainty. For example, construction estimates are often exceeded. If a company's history of construction costs is that 90 percent of its estimates have been exceeded by 15 percent, then in a capital estimate there is every justification for increasing the value of this factor by 15 percent. This is a matter of improving the accuracy of the estimate.

But suppose that new-product sales estimates have been exceeded by more than 75 percent in one-fourth of all historical cases and have not reached 50 percent of the estimate in one-sixth of all such cases. Because penalties for overestimating are very tangible, management is apt to reduce the sales estimate to "cover" the one case in six, thereby reducing the calculated rate of return. In doing so, it may miss some of its best opportunities.

3. *Revising cutoff rates.* By selecting higher cutoff rates to protect against uncertainty, management is attempting to do much the same thing. Management would like to have a possibility of return that is in proportion to the risk it takes. Where there is much uncertainty involved in the various estimates of sales, costs, prices, and so on, a high calculated return from the investment provides some incentive for taking the risk. This is, in fact, a perfectly sound position. The trouble is that the decision maker still needs to know explicitly what risks he is taking—and what the odds are on achieving the expected return.

4. *Three-level estimates.* A start at spelling out risks, as noted earlier, is sometimes made by taking the high, medium, and low values of the estimated factors and calculating rates of return based on various combinations of the pessimistic, average, and optimistic estimates. These calculations give a picture of the range of possible results but do not tell the executive whether the pessimistic result is more likely than the optimistic one—or, in fact, whether the

average result is much more likely to occur than either of the extremes. So, although this is a step in the right direction, it still does not give a clear enough picture for comparing alternatives.

5. *Selected probabilities.* Various methods have been used to include the probabilities of specific factors in the return calculation. These are helpful and tend to clarify the executive's view of investment alternatives. But they do not define the range of "risk taken" or "return hoped for" closely enough to help very much in the complex decisions of capital planning.

6. *Trying to force a solution.* A completely different course that seems to have special appeal to marketing-oriented companies is sometimes followed. A company following this course will freely acknowledge all the uncertainties surrounding the estimated outcome of a new investment—and then brush them aside on the grounds that the actual outcome can be "forced" to fit the estimate. For example, if sales fall short of the target, various measures ranging from heavier advertising to a shake-up of the sales force can be used to get the desired results. And since the precise circumstances in which these tactics might have to be applied cannot be known in advance, there is no point in worrying until the time comes: "Something will always turn up." Of course, such a Micawberish view completely misses the point. If one can be *certain* of achieving a particular set of results, the uncertainty disappears—and so, in large measure, does the problem of investment policy. In this case, the "self-healing" properties of many business situations can and should be taken into account.[4] But if one cannot do so, the uncertainty and the problem remain. And the striking proportion of marketing failures belies the optimism of the Micawbers.

SHARPENING THE PICTURE

Since every one of the many factors that enter into the evaluation of a specific decision is subject to some uncertainty, the executive needs to know the effects that the uncertainty surrounding each of the significant factors has on the returns he is likely to achieve.

---

[4] For example, a new product line can be programmed to match sales as they grow, taking a hedge on the early risk in the form of higher initial production costs. Or the option may be kept open to sell off a capital asset in order to cut losses to a minimum.

Therefore, the risk analysis method combines the variabilities of all the relevant factors. The objective is to give a clear picture of the relative risk and the probable odds of coming out ahead or behind in the light of uncertain foreknowledge.

A simulation of the way these factors may combine as the future unfolds is the key to extracting the maximum information from the available forecasts. In fact, the approach is very straightforward, using a computer to do the arithmetic.

To carry out the analysis, a company must follow three steps:

1. Estimate the range of values for each of the factors (e.g., range of selling price, sales growth rate), and within that range, estimate the likelihood of occurrence of each value.

2. Select one particular value at random from the distribution of values for each factor. Then combine the values for all of the factors and compute the rate of return (or present value) for that combination. For instance, the lowest in the range of prices might be combined with the highest in the range of growth rate and other factors. (The fact that some factors are mutually dependent should be taken into account, as we shall see later.)

3. Do this over and over again to define and evaluate the odds of the occurrence of each possible rate of return. Since there are literally millions of possible combinations of values, the likelihood of various specific returns on the investment must be tested. This is like finding out by recording the results of a great many throws what percentage of sevens or other combinations we may expect in tossing dice. The result will be a listing of the rates of return that can be achieved, ranging from a loss (if the factors go against us) to whatever maximum gain is possible with the estimates that have been made.

The chances of the occurrence of each of these rates are determined. (Remember that a specific return can usually be achieved through more than one combination of events. The more combinations for a given rate, the higher the chances of achieving it—as with sevens in tossing dice.) As we have seen, the average expectation is the average of the values of all outcomes weighted by each outcome's chances of occurring.

The variability from the average of outcome values is also determined. This is important because, all other factors being equal, management would presumably prefer lower variability for the same return if given the choice. The use of this concept to help decide on policies for choosing investments will be discussed later. (When the expected return and variability of each of a series of investments have been determined, the same techniques may be used to examine how effectively various combinations of these investments will meet management objectives.)

PRACTICAL TEST

To see how this approach works in practice, one can use as a basis of comparison the experience of a management that has already analyzed a specific investment proposal by conventional techniques. Taking the same investment schedule and the same expected values actually used, one can find what results the new method would produce and compare them with the results obtained when conventional methods were applied. As will be seen, the new picture of risks and returns is different from the old one. Yet the differences are in no way attributable to changes in the basic data; they are attributable only to the fact that this method is more sensitive to management's uncertainties about the key factors.

Investment proposal

In this case, a medium-sized industrial chemical producer is considering an extension to its processing plant that is estimated to cost $10 million. The estimated service life of the facility is ten years; the engineers expect to be able to utilize 250,000 tons of processed material estimated to be worth $510 per ton at an average processing cost of $435 per ton. Is this investment a good bet? In fact, what is the return that the company may expect? What are the risks? The best and fullest use must be made of all the market research and financial analyses that have been developed. Management can then have a clear picture of this project despite uncertainties.

The key input factors that management has decided to use are:
1. Market size
2. Selling prices
3. Market growth rate
4. Share of market (that results in physical sales volume)
5. Investment required
6. Residual value of investment

7. Operating costs
8. Fixed costs
9. Useful life of facilities

These factors are typical of those in many company projects that must be analyzed and combined to obtain a measure of the attractiveness of a proposed capital facilities investment.

Obtaining estimates

How can this proposal be analyzed in the recommended way? The goal is to develop for each of the nine factors listed a frequency distribution or probability curve. The information needed includes the possible ranges of values for each factor, the average value for each factor, and some ideas of the likelihood that the various possible values will be reached. For major capital proposals, management usually makes a significant investment in time and funds to pinpoint information about each of the relevant factors. An objective analysis of the values to be assigned to each can, with some additional effort, yield a subjective probability distribution.

Specifically, it is necessary to probe and question each of the experts involved—to find out, for example, whether the estimated cost of production really can be said to be exactly a certain value or whether, as is more likely, the cost should be estimated to lie within a certain range of values. That range is often ignored in analysis, but it is relatively easy to determine, and if one has to guess—as one often does—a range is easier to guess with some accuracy than is a specific single value. As a rule, discussion of such distributions in a series of meetings with management personnel is most helpful in reaching realistic answers to the a priori questions. (The term "realistic answers" implies that the assumptions underlying the analysis are clearly spelled out.)

The ranges are directly related to the degree of confidence that the estimator has in his estimate. Thus, certain estimates may be known to be quite accurate. They would be represented by probability distributions stating, for instance, that there is only 1 chance in 10 that the actual value will differ from the best estimate by more than 10 percent of the estimate. Others may range as much as 100 percent above and below the best estimate.

Thus, one treats the factor of selling price for the finished product by determining from the executives (who are responsible for the original estimates) answers to questions such as:

1. Given an expected sales price of $510, what is the probability that the price will exceed $550?
2. Is there any chance that the price will exceed $650?
3. How likely is it that the price will drop below $475?

Management must have answers to similar questions for each of the other factors; a distribution or probability curve can then be constructed for each. This is not so difficult as it might sound. Often information on the degree of variation is readily available; e.g., historical data on commodity price variations. Similarly, management can estimate the variability of sales from industry sales records. Even for factors that have no history, such as operating costs for a new product, the person who makes the "average" estimate can usually indicate the degree of confidence he has in his prediction. The less confidence he has in his estimate, the greater will be the range of possible values that the variable will assume.

This last point is likely to trouble businessmen. Does it really make sense to seek estimates of variations? It cannot be emphasized too strongly that the less certainty there is in an "average" estimate, *the more important it is to consider the possible variation in that estimate.*

Further, an estimate of the variation that is possible in a factor, no matter how judgmental it may be, is always better than a simple "average" estimate, since it includes more information about both what is known and what is not known. In fact, because this lack of knowledge is in itself important information about the proposed investment, it may distinguish one investment possibility from another. Therefore, what is not known must be taken into account if decision making is to be rational.

To throw any information away simply because it is highly uncertain is a serious error in analysis, which the risk analysis approach is designed to correct.

Computer runs

The next step in the proposed approach is to determine the returns that will result from random combinations of the factors involved. A flow chart of the factors and the way they combine and interact to produce the end result (e.g., revenues, costs, investments) must be developed. This requires realistic restrictions, such as not allowing the total market to vary more than some reasonable amount from year to year. Of course, any method of rating the return that is suitable to the company may be used at this point; in the actual case being described here, management preferred discounted cash flow for the reasons cited earlier.

This flow chart must then be programmed for a computer that can carry out the trials for the simulation method rapidly and at low cost. For one trial actually made in this case, 3,600 discounted cash flow calculations, each based on a selection of the nine input factors, were run in two minutes at a minimal cost for computer time. The resulting rate-of-return probabilities were read out immediately and graphed. The process is shown schematically in Figure 5-3.

Data comparisons

The nine input factors just mentioned fall into three categories:

1. *Market analyses to determine revenues.* Factors included are market size, market growth rate, the firm's share of the market, and selling prices. For a given combination of these factors, sales revenue may be determined.

2. *Capital investment cost analyses.* This category includes investment required, residual value of investment, and useful life of facilities. Being tied to the kinds of service life and operating-cost characteristics expected, these factors are subject to various kinds of error and uncertainty; for instance, automation progress makes service life uncertain.

3. *Operating and fixed costs analyses.* Operating and fixed costs also are subject to uncertainty but are perhaps the easiest to estimate.

These three categories are not independent of each other; for realistic results, the approach allows the various factors to be tied together through the flow chart and thence through the computer program. Thus, if price determines the total market, the price for the specific computer run is first selected from a probability distribution, and a probability distribution that is logically related to the price selection is then used for the total market.

The values obtained through the new approach can now be

Simulation for Investment Planning

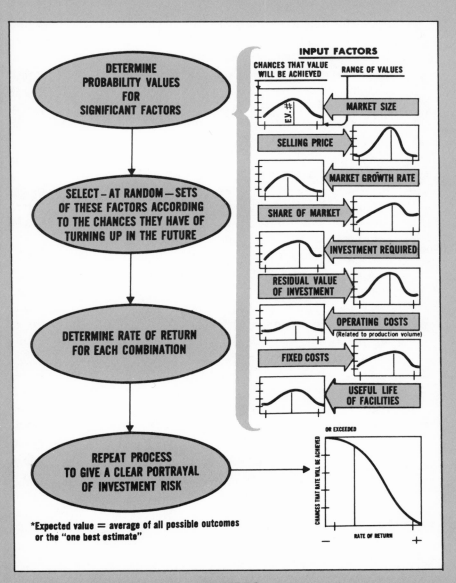

FIGURE 5-3

compared with the values obtained through the old. This comparison is shown in Figure 5-4.

Valuable results

How do the results obtained through the new and old approaches compare? In this case, management had been informed, on the basis of the "one best estimate" approach, that the expected return was 25.2 percent before taxes. When the new set of data was run through the computer program, however, the expected return was only 14.6 percent before taxes. This surprising difference is due not only to the fact that under the new approach a range of values was used but also to the fact that each value in the range had been weighed on the basis of its chances of occurring.

The new analysis thus may help management either to avoid an unwise investment or to make a good one. In fact, carefully weighing the information and lack of information about investment proposals in the manner suggested generally indicates the underlying uncertainty of the available information about otherwise seemingly satisfactory or poor investment proposals.

The computer program developed to carry out the simulation can allow for easy insertion of new variables. Further, for each repetition in the simulation of outcomes, the program can permit the choice of a value for price from one distribution: a value that will then determine the particular probability distribution (from among several) that will be used to determine the value for sales volume to be used with the selected price.

To understand how this important technique works, suppose there is a wheel, as in roulette, with the numbers from 0 to 5 representing one price for the product or material, the numbers 6 to 12 representing a second price, the numbers 13 to 25 a third price, and so on. For each of these segments there would be a different range of expected market volumes; e.g., $150,000 to $200,000 for the first, $100,000 to $150,000 for the second, $75,000 to $100,000 for the third. Now suppose the wheel is spun and the ball falls in 17. This would mean that a sales volume in the $75,000 to $100,000 range has been picked. If the ball goes in 1, there is a different price and the sales volume is in the $150,000 to $200,000 range.

Most significant, perhaps, is the fact that the program allows management to ascertain the sensitivity of the results to each or all

Comparison of Expected Values Under Old and New Approaches

	Conventional 'best estimate' approach	RANGE* OF ESTIMATED VALUES		
		LOW	MID	HIGH
MARKET ANALYSES				
1. MARKET SIZE (tons 000)	250	100	250	340
2. SELLING PRICES ($/ton)	$510	$385	$510	$575
3. MARKET GROWTH RATE	3%	0%	3%	6%
4. EVENTUAL SHARE OF MARKET	12%	3%	12%	17%
INVESTMENT COST ANALYSES				
5. TOTAL INVESTMENT REQUIRED (Millions)	$9.5	$7.0	$9.5	$10.5
6. USEFUL LIFE OF FACILITIES (Years)	10	5	10	15
7. RESIDUAL VALUE (at 10 years) (Millions)	$4.5	$3.5	$4.5	$5.0
OTHER COSTS				
8. OPERATING COSTS ($/ton)	$435	$370	$435	$545
9. FIXED COSTS ($000)	$300	$250	$300	$375
EXPECTED VALUE OF ROI %	25.2	14.6		

*Range figures represent approximately 1% to 99% probabilities. That is, there is only a 1 in 100 chance that the value actually achieved will be respectively greater or less than the range.

FIGURE 5-4

Anticipated Rates of Return Under Old and New Approaches

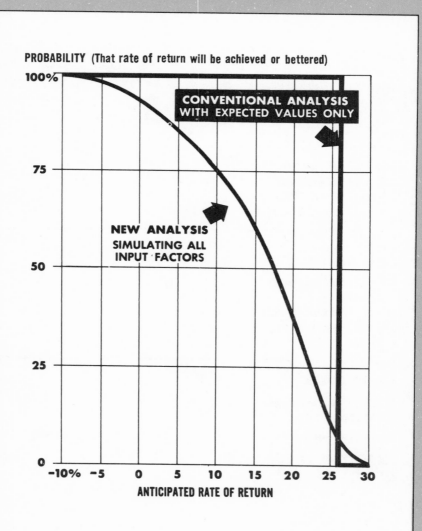

FIGURE 5-5

of the input factors. Simply by running the program with changes in the distribution of an input factor, it is possible to determine the effect of added or changed information (or lack of information). It may turn out that fairly large changes in some factors do not significantly affect the outcome. In the case being described, as a matter of fact, management was particularly concerned about the difficulty of estimating market growth. Running the program with variations in this factor quickly demonstrated that for average annual growths ranging from 3 percent to 5 percent there was no significant difference in the expected outcome.

In addition, one can see the implications of the detailed knowledge provided by the simulation method. Using single expected values, management arrives only at a hoped-for expectation of 25.2 percent after taxes (which, as has been seen, is wrong unless there is no variability in the various input factors—a highly unlikely event). On the other hand, with the method outlined here, the uncertainties are clearly portrayed.

Percent return	*Probability of achieving* *at least the return shown*
0	96.5%
5	80.6
10	75.2
15	53.8
20	43.0
25	12.6
30	0.0

This profile is shown in Figure 5-5. Such a graph, showing percent probability of realizing various returns, is a "risk profile" like the profiles briefly discussed in Chapter 4. Note the contrast with the profile obtained under the conventional approach. This concept can be used for evaluation of new-product introductions, acquisitions of new businesses, and plant modernization—in other words, whenever management is faced with risky investment choices.

CHAPTER 6
Designing Capital Investment Programs

THE most important question management faces in deciding whether to continue investing in its going businesses and whether to invest in new opportunities is: "What information is needed to clarify the key differences among various alternatives over the planning horizon?" The basic factors that should be considered in the case of each business—markets, prices, costs, and so on—are already agreed on. Also, the way the future return on investment should be calculated is, if not agreed on, at least limited to a few methods, any of which can be consistently used by a given company. If the input variables turn out as estimated, any of the methods customarily used to rate investments should provide satisfactory (though not necessarily optimum) returns.

In actual practice, however, the conventional methods do *not* work out satisfactorily. Why? The reason, as seen in the preceding chapter, and as every executive and economist knows, is that the estimates used in making projections are just that—estimates. More accurate estimates would be helpful, but residual uncertainty can still make a mockery of corporate hopes. Yet, as we have seen, there is a solution. Providing realistic estimates for the key factors requires an in-depth analysis of each factor to ascertain the uncertainties involved, as well as the reasons for these uncertainties. Using this knowledge of uncertainty, executives can maximize the value of the information for decision making.

The value of computer programs in developing clear portrayals of the uncertainty and risk surrounding individual investments has been clearly demonstrated. Such programs can produce valuable information about the sensitivity of the possible outcomes to the variability of input factors and to the likelihood of achieving various possible rates of return. This information can be an extremely important backup to management judgment. Decision makers are more confident that the available information has been used with maximum efficiency when they have calculations of the odds on all possible outcomes.

This simulation approach has the inherent advantages of completeness and simplicity. It requires only an extension of the input estimates (to the best of one's ability) in terms of probabilities. No variable should be projected as a single value—the equivalent of saying we know it with pinpoint accuracy—unless we are *certain* of it.

The very discipline of thinking through the uncertainties of the problem helps to ensure better investment decisions. To understand uncertainty and risk is to understand a key business problem —and the key business opportunity. The risk analysis approach can be applied on a continuing basis to each capital alternative as it comes up for consideration and progresses toward fruition. Gradual progress toward reducing the uncertainty of estimates may therefore be expected as experience is gained in a given project or set of projects.

There is no doubt that courage to act boldly in the face of apparent uncertainty can be greatly bolstered by the clear portrayal of the risks and possible rewards. To achieve this security requires only a slight effort beyond what most companies already exert in studying capital investments.

REMAINING INVESTMENT
PLANNING PROBLEMS

Risk analysis of investment alternatives cannot solve broad company investment policy problems. The remaining problems —e.g., what cutoff rates should be used to optimize overall returns, and how specific projects should be selected—are serious, as shown in the following testimony:

- The president of a big international corporation told the writer, "I can't understand why our investment policy hasn't worked the way we expected." Some years ago, the president explained, the executive committee had decided that every capital investment must meet the test of an estimated before-tax average annual return on capital of 20 percent. The rule had been scrupulously followed, yet actual results had averaged 14 percent. "And we've got some of the best analysts in the business," added the frustrated president.

- In another large and sophisticated company engaged in diversified manufacturing operations, barely half of the new investments made over the past ten years are now expected to reach break-even—and less than half of these will reach or exceed their predicted return on investment. On the other hand, returns of some of the winners will be much larger than anticipated.

- The executive committee of a major chemical company is facing a real dilemma. The committee currently requires each proposed capital project to show an expected return of at least 12 percent after taxes (16 percent for high-risk investments). Applying this policy, the executive committee has not turned down a single capital investment proposal in the past two years. Results from recent investments, however, have been alarmingly uneven. To provide a better screen for future proposals and, hopefully, to improve investment results, a new policy requiring a three-year payback period plus a discounted cash flow return of 8 percent has been recommended to the committee. They do not know what to do.

However, management science methods, using systematic analysis and computer simulation of the investment process, will help most companies to choose the policies and plans that are most likely to meet their objectives. Specifically, these methods allow management to answer the following questions confidently:

■ Historically, has our investment policy given us the highest possible return from our investments, consistent with the risks we have accepted?

■ How much risk have we been accepting in our investment decisions? Is this consistent with the risks top management really wants to accept?

■ Have we been using the best criteria for investment selection, considering long-term corporate objectives? Have we been taking adequate account of uncertainty?

And, finally, the key question:

■ Given the investment alternatives that are available to us and the risks we are willing to accept, what investment policy will maximize the earnings-per-share performance of our investments over the long run?

RISK AND THE FUTURE

As has already been illustrated, uncertainty creates risk. The exact course of future events is unknown when investment choices are made. Yet risk analysis can show management the "betting odds" on future risks. Risk profiles can be developed for any criterion that management may wish to use. For example, Figure 6-1 shows the payback, average ROI (return on investment), and discounted ROI profiles of a hypothetical investment.

Of two investments, one is clearly the better if it offers a greater probability of achieving any given level of return. In this situation, risk analysis permits management to distinguish without question the more from the less desirable investments. In Figure 6-2, for example, investment A is clearly a better bet than investment B at all values of return; that is, it dominates investment B.

But one investment alternative is not always dominant. Consider the case of investments X and Y in the same exhibit. Here, investment X is more likely than investment Y to attain a 10 percent return on investment but less likely to bring in a 40 percent

Risk-Analysis Results for a Specific Investment for 3 Criteria

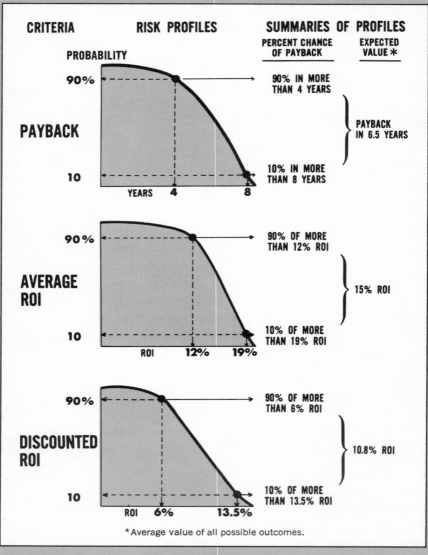

*Average value of all possible outcomes.

FIGURE 6-1

Investment Risk Profiles

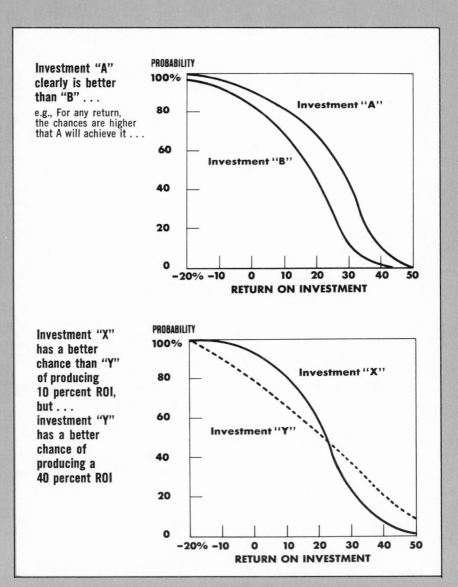

FIGURE 6-2

return. In the numerous cases of this kind, the question of which investment to select, or even of how to go about establishing a policy to guide the choice, has hitherto gone unanswered.

To be sure, in using risk profiles management avails itself of all the quantitative information that can be put together on the investment possibilities. And more information in the hands of management should mean better decisions. Yet the question of how to put this information to effective use remains. Before it can be answered, the nature and function of an investment policy must be understood.

THE FUNCTION OF AN INVESTMENT POLICY

Maintaining the earning power of assets on a satisfactory level— keeping them competitive by investing in established businesses, making them increase by investing in new businesses—is the task to which management applies an investment policy and a long-range plan.

Any investment policy, if it is to guide management's choices among available investment alternatives, must embody two components: (1) *one or more criteria* by which to measure the relative economic attributes of investment alternatives; and (2) *decision rules*—which may or may not make use of risk analysis or otherwise seek to take uncertainty into account—for selecting "acceptable" investments.

The criteria have been the subject of much analysis and discussion. They include the payback period, which is simply the number of years required for the investment to return its costs; average annual percent return on average funds employed; net present value measures; and internal rates of return, calculated on a discounted cash flow basis. On the other hand, the rules for making choices, particularly under uncertainty, have been largely unformulated. Of course, no preestablished policy can take into account all the considerations—human, organizational, strategic, and financial—that typically enter into a major capital investment decision. On the other hand, there are specific elements of financial policy that do lend themselves to rigorous formulation.

A consistent and adequate investment policy has a double function. In the short run, it should indicate which investments should be chosen to achieve the financial objectives of the corporation. In the long run, it should serve as a basis for identifying or developing investment alternatives that are likely to match the policies selected. In other words, it serves as a basis both for (1) *acting on* and (2) *communicating about* investment alternatives.

In the first instance, an investment policy may be regarded as a screen that will "pass" certain investment proposals and reject others. What the screen passes and rejects depends on management's knowing or unknowing choice. It will pass the investment proposals that management finds acceptable; these proposals will form management's "investment potential set." Risks (whether calculated or not) attach to all investments, and the profiles of these risks *vary with the criteria chosen to measure their attractiveness* even though the different profiles are based upon the same estimates of underlying real-world phenomena. It then becomes clear that a policy with a "determinate," or single-point-based, decision-rule component [1] is a very coarse screen indeed, if it can be called a screen at all. In any case, as many companies have found, such a "determinate" policy is ineffective. It will not help management to make the best use of its investment funds, no matter what the company's financial objectives may be.

Risk-based policies, on the other hand, may specify how management would prefer to trade off the chances of low return against the chances of high return. For example, would it prefer a virtual certainty of no loss coupled with a virtual ceiling on gains over 20 percent after taxes—or would it accept a 1-in-10 chance of significant loss for the sake of a 1-in-10 chance of very high gain?

A specific policy may be defined by the criteria to be used and the rules to be followed in screening investments (in this case, in terms of their risk profiles—as in the following example):

1. *Criterion to be used as a measure of investment worth*
   —Before-tax return on investment, on a discounted cash flow basis
2. *Rules to be used to screen investments based on risk profiles of proposed projects*
   —Accept proposals that have:

---

[1] For example, "Accept all investment proposals that show a projected return of more than 12 percent on the investment after taxes."

i)	Expected value (average of all outcomes)	10% (minimum)
ii)	One out of ten chances that the ROI will exceed	25%
iii)	Nine out of ten chances that the ROI will exceed	0%

These rules, which make explicit management's entrepreneurial or risk-taking attitudes, do allow consistent investment choices. The methods described here assume that uncertainty (i.e., the spread of distribution of potential returns around the "expected value," or average of all outcomes) is a useful measure of risk. Generally, the greater the margin by which the return could exceed the "expected value," the greater the margin by which it could fall short—and lucky indeed is the company to which this principle does not apply!

In addition, an investment policy can be a powerful communications tool, enabling top management to make known in advance to those responsible for developing investment proposals what sort of projects the company seeks. The object is to control the selection and development of alternatives so that they reflect the gains the company wants to make and the risks it is willing to undergo to achieve them.

In theory, of course, this function could be served by policy statements such as: "All investments must have an estimated average return on capital employed of 12 percent or more after taxes." But, in practical terms, the complexity of most present-day investment projects and the multitude of future variables to which they are subject rob such statements of most of their usefulness. This is why top managment today, confronted with requests for capital, so often finds that the only significant response it can make is to approve the results of all the analysis that has previously taken place at divisional and staff levels.

With a risk-based policy using one or more criteria and rules such as those in the preceding example, management still has no guarantee that all or any of the available investments will pass through the screen. It does, however, have a better, more specific means for discriminating among proposed investments. It also has a tool for testing its own procedures for developing investment proposals and for checking alternative plans for the future. To analyze its future investments in its established lines of business, as well as requests for capital in new businesses, a company can estimate the uncertainty profiles for revenues, costs, and capital requirements of these investments and can determine what changes in the selected mix would be indicated by different policy choices.

This analysis, however, still will not indicate what is the best overall investment policy; i.e., what impact the choice of a particular criterion such as net present value, payback, or return on investment will have on the likely outcome of specific real-world variables such as costs and revenues,[2] or what differences there are (again, in terms of real-world financial results) between high-risk and low-risk screens.

THE CONCEPT OF EFFICIENCY

Most managements would like to have investment policies that maximize financial results over the long run while minimizing uncertainty or risk. Seeking additional returns, however, normally entails accepting additional uncertainty—i.e., risk. If two policies produce the same average result (e.g., the same average earnings per share over a five-year period), the one that involves less variability (or uncertainty as to the outcome) for the same yield is a more desirable or "efficient" policy. Conversely, of two policies entailing the same variability, the one producing the higher expected return ("expected" meaning the average of all outcomes) is obviously the better policy. "Variability" is best measured by the spread of values within which the probable results are likely to fall. Thus, the spread or variability of a risk profile can be measured by the size of the standard deviation.[3]

When the financial results of investments selected on the basis of a particular policy are simulated, the expected return along with the standard deviation of the financial results obtained with that

[2] Note that the criteria of attractiveness are mathematically derived in fairly complicated ways from real-world events such as sales, price changes, and equipment installations. Since the uncertainty profiles of the events must be used to determine the final "risk profile" of the criterion, simulation methods are required.

[3] This statistical measure represents the spread around the expected value of the criterion containing approximately two-thirds of all probable outcomes.

policy will indicate the "efficiency" of the investment project set selected under that policy.

The expected return and the standard deviation can be plotted on a graph to show the effectiveness of any policy, and a line can then be drawn through the points of greatest yield for a given standard deviation. This line may be called the *efficiency frontier,* because it represents the best return on investment that management can get at a given degree of risk.

Figure 6-3 illustrates how the average returns (in this case, earnings per share) are plotted against the standard deviation of these earnings to give an efficiency frontier. Each point on the graph represents the financial results to be expected from a combination of investments selected by passing the same group of investment proposals through the screen of a particular investment policy. (These results were obtained by simulating fifteen years of the operation of a company using this policy.)

Policies A, B, and C lie on the efficiency frontier because each produces the maximum earnings per share for a given degree of risk. Policies D, E, and F do not lie on the frontier because none of them produces, for a given standard deviation, as much earnings as management could obtain by using a different policy. Policy F, for example, is better than E because it earns $4.00 while E earns $2.95 for the same risk (15 percent standard deviation), but it is worse than A, which produces earnings of $6.50 at a standard deviation of 16 percent. An efficient policy at 15 percent standard deviation could produce average earnings of approximately $6.25 per share. (Specific policies can be developed to fill in the entire efficiency frontier curve.)

Granting that the objective of an investment policy is to maximize average long-term earnings or yield for a given variation of those earnings or of that yield, there is no reason why a management that has calculated its own efficiency frontier should use policies other than those on that frontier. Other policies would entail more uncertain investment results, and/or lower expected returns, than the company need accept. A management that wants to invest rationally—i.e., wants to optimize results—has every reason, therefore, to locate its efficiency frontier, the point on that frontier at which it wishes to operate and then continually strive to improve it.

Comparing Effectiveness of Investment Policies

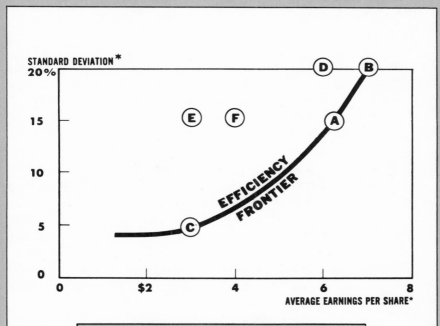

SIMULATION RESULTS		
POLICY	AVERAGE EARNINGS PER SHARE*	STANDARD DEVIATION*
A	$6.50	16%
B	7.10	20
C	3.00	5
D	5.75	20
E	2.95	15
F	4.00	15

*Under reasonable assumptions of depreciation, life of investments, initial conditions, etc., standard deviation given as percentage of average value.

FIGURE 6-3

PROBABILISTIC LONG-RANGE PLANNING

How practicable is the concept of "efficient" investment sets (on the efficiency frontier) and how "effective" will the investment policies be that choose such sets? In terms of actual investment results, what light does the efficient investment set concept throw on the choice of particular investment criteria such as payback period or average annual return? To help answer these questions, some companies are using computer models that make it possible to simulate the effects that various policies would have, over a period of years, on the company's financial results.

In the simulation model, generally acceptable accounting procedures are used to determine financial results. Straight-line depreciation or other appropriate depreciation methods may be used, and dividend policies may be tested, along with whatever debt is considered appropriate in the particular year.

In one such model, used to test various investment policies, three sets of thirty-seven hypothetical investments were used as inputs. Each of these hypothetical investments, in turn, was characterized by a particular set of uncertainty profiles for the three key variables for each year of the particular investment: sales, costs, and investment requirements.

The computer simulation then involved seven steps:

1. Choosing an investment policy for test by:

    a. Selecting a financial criterion (or criteria).

    b. Establishing decision rules. Except in the case of single-point estimates, these rules specified criterion values at the 10 percent and 90 percent probability points on the criterion risk profile, as well as a minimum average value (see, for example, policy described on pages 93–94).

2. Developing risk profiles for each investment from the uncertainty profiles of key variables for each investment given in the available investment set.

3. Screening investments against policy and accepting all those that pass the screen, observing realistic constraints on the size and number of investments to be made in a given year.

4. Simulating the financial performance of the chosen investments over a fifteen-year period: randomly selecting the operating results for each year from the individual uncertainty profiles for the investment project, in order to obtain one set of operating results of that investment for each year.

5. Combining the various revenues, costs, and investment requirements for each of the years, and then computing the yearly financial results for this investment "set."

6. Repeating the entire process until a stable distribution of the financial results for the policy chosen and the investments available had been built up. Determining the average or expected value and the standard deviation of the key financial results.

7. Repeating the first six steps for other policies and other sets of investment alternatives.

For each of the three investment sets, investment policies embodying conservative, medium-risk, and high-risk screens for various criteria [4] were tested. The conservative policies required a very high probability of no loss along with moderate expectations, while the high-risk policies accepted significant chances of loss but required good chances of high gains. Single-point determinate policies were also included in the tests. The investments available were varied and realistic, ranging from short-term to long-term payouts, with cash investment requirements sometimes extending into later years. The simulation was repeated 500 times for each policy and for each set of investments, and the financial results were calculated for each year of a fifteen-year period. The average and the standard deviation of each financial result were determined for each year and for the combination of the last five years of the runs. The results of all the runs support at least four general conclusions:

1. There is a wide gap in financial performance between some commonly used investment policies and policies that lie on the "efficiency frontier."

2. Risk-based policies consistently give better results than those using single-point, determinate decision rules. Using determinate decision rules, one cannot compensate for high risk by raising the level-of-return hurdle; single-point estimate screens produce, at

[4] Payback, average annual proceeds as a percentage of the investment, discounted return on investment, net present value.

best, half the return for a given degree of risk, no matter how the required return level is raised or lowered.

3. Long-term financial results are highly dependent on the risk accepted for a given return, or of return achieved for a given degree of risk. Thus, on the efficiency frontier, to get a long-term average return of $6 per share management would have to accept fluctuations on the order of plus or minus 45 percent in two years out of three, whereas it could get only $3.75 if it decided to accept a probable fluctuation no greater than 10 percent.

4. Some investment criteria are empirically better than others. Whenever growth is a goal, i.e., whenever results are measured on an earnings-per-share basis, net present value (NPV) and discounted internal rate of return (ROI-dcf)—both based on discounting future returns [5]—are superior to criteria, such as average annual return, that do not take the time value of money into account. At 25 percent annual standard deviation, for example (i.e., accepting a 1-in-3 chance that the results will fall outside plus or minus 25 percent of the expected values in any given year), the discounting criterion gives expected earnings per share of $5.50 while the nondiscounted criterion gives $4.10! Moreover, payback period—still an extremely popular criterion—turns out to be an extremely crude, inconsistent, and inefficient yardstick from the standpoint of actual financial results. All the investments selected with payback criteria showed higher variances and lower returns than the others.

A more general conclusion to be drawn from this simulation model is that management can profitably use the same approach to evaluate all its plans, determine its efficiency frontier, and consciously select efficient investment policies that more accurately reflect its risk preference.

Note that the results for analyzing probable fluctuations in earnings ($3.40 per share) shown in Figure 6-4 are charted in terms of standard deviation; i.e., the vertical coordinate of any point on

[5] Policies that produce equivalent financial results for net present value (NPV) and the discounted internal rate of return (ROI-dcf) can be developed. In other words, it is possible to assign specific values to (1) the discount rate, and (2) the probability that the net present value of the cash-flow stream will be a given ratio of the net present value of the investment, so as to obtain an NPV screen for investments exactly equivalent to specific risk-based values of the ROI-dcf criterion.

Determining Probable
Fluctuations of Earnings

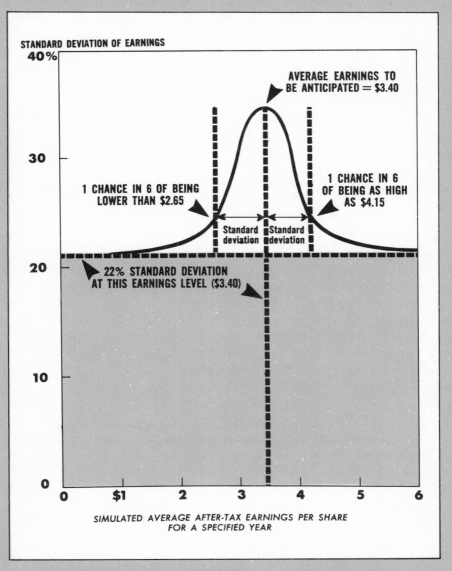

STANDARD DEVIATION OF EARNINGS

AVERAGE EARNINGS TO
BE ANTICIPATED = $3.40

1 CHANCE IN 6 OF BEING
LOWER THAN $2.65

1 CHANCE IN 6
OF BEING AS HIGH
AS $4.15

Standard deviation | Standard deviation

22% STANDARD DEVIATION
AT THIS EARNINGS LEVEL ($3.40)

SIMULATED AVERAGE AFTER-TAX EARNINGS PER SHARE
FOR A SPECIFIED YEAR

FIGURE 6-4

the chart represents the range of variation in results that may be expected approximately *two-thirds of the time* from a particular policy (plus or minus $0.75). If management is unwilling to accept 1 chance in 6 of results falling below the lower value of this range ($2.65), it may have to accept a lower average return than the $3.40 per share earnings indicated. In fact, since the variation or distribution of values around this average is "normal" [6] (being the arithmetic sum of all the various "non-normal" distributions that are involved in doing business), each point on the earnings average versus standard deviation graph can be analyzed to determine the likelihood of a specific fluctuation of earnings in a specific year. Clearly, the job of a growth-minded, forward-looking management is to keep the earnings up while pushing the standard deviations down.[7]

If a company pushes for higher stable earnings, it must constantly examine its investment of assets in current going businesses and its available choices for investing in new projects. But, as noted, unless each project is examined to determine how sure management's projected earnings are likely to be, the decision-making process is severely handicapped. Continuing investments in old assets are, of course, subject to the same vicissitudes and should be similarly examined.

However, the examination of each individual project does not in itself assure that risks will be kept under control while earnings are pushed up. The corporate model discussed previously permits the combination of investments to show their profit and loss and balance sheet consequences. How can this model be used for long-range planning to attain specific corporate goals?

It is both theoretically and empirically true that if we combine two unrelated or independent risky bets, the variability of the joint

[6] The statisticians' gaussian distribution or the so-called "bell-shaped" curve.

[7] Note that this is very closely related to investment portfolio management. The same choices between earnings, growth, and stability must be made. H. M. Markowitz pioneered in discussing the portfolio problem in *Portfolio Selection* (John Wiley & Sons, Inc., New York, 1959). Considerable work has been done since, including that of F. S. Hillier, "The Evaluation of Risky Interrelated Investments," Technical Report No. 73, Department of Statistics, Stanford University, July, 1964. And more recently, Kalman J. Cohen and Edwin J. Elton in "Inter-Temporal Portfolio Analysis Based on Simulation of Joint Returns" in *Management Science*, vol. 14, no. 1, September, 1967, have developed a model similar in nature and function to that described here.

end result is greater than the variability of either alone. And, of course, this makes sense—as the usual odds on the daily double at a racetrack illustrate. If there were not something else involved, this principle could mean that all of management's planning would be useless: as executives approved more and more investments, up would go the risks. There are two other things that prevent this from happening. Both are well known to management, and both can be incorporated into the corporate planning model, which can then be used to strengthen the future position of the company.

These two "variability control" factors rely on the fact that capital investments are not mutually independent. They either (1) depend on the same economic factors to move in the same or opposite directions (cyclical or countercyclical investments) or (2) affect one another directly (positive or negative synergy).

The corporate planning model can take both of these factors into account. One direct way, diagramed in Figure 6-5, is to analyze a company as a series of going businesses and project for each its uncertainty profiles of costs, revenues, and investment requirements for several years ahead—a decade, say. Uncertainty profiles can also be projected for the major alternative new streams of businesses. These should all be connected to appropriate overall projections (also on a probabilistic basis) of measures of the business cycle (GNP, carloadings, or other), some to shift upward, some downward, depending on what is called for. And the model provides for "synergistic" connections between specific businesses or new endeavors. For example, it would determine the profitability of using an existing sales force if a new product line were added to a present business segment, or the value of using an existing production facility to carry out some part of a manufacturing process in a newly added business.

Using this model, management can examine alternative planning decisions at any point in time and choose those that will most probably provide the desired earnings stream with an acceptable degree of risk or variability.

CONCLUSION

Computer simulation thus offers corporate management, for the first time, a tool that will enable it to examine the consequences of

Corporate Planning Model for Simulating Action Alternatives

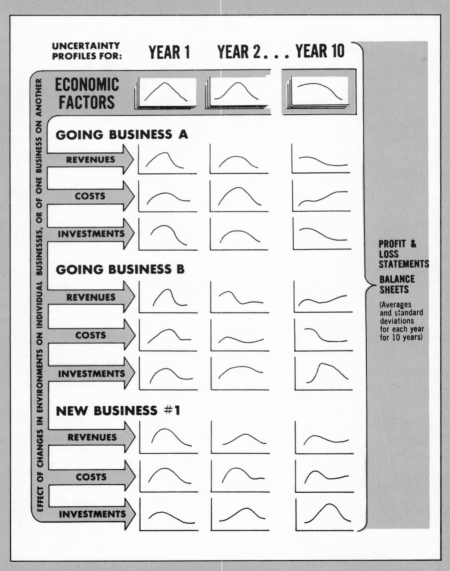

FIGURE 6-5

various investment policies and plans. As the research reported here has shown, the use of a corporate planning model and the application of management science methods to investment choices involve four requirements:

1. The determination of risk profiles for all investments—and present businesses

2. The use of a discounting measure for the merit of an investment proposal (either discounted internal rate of return or an equivalent net present value)

3. The establishment of alternative screening rules for investment proposals

4. The determination of risk boundaries for the alternative policies and the alternative combinations of investments

A company should be able to determine the level of investment in each class of businesses and proposed projects that will combine with investment levels and risks in other classes to maximize the company's chances of achieving long-range corporate growth goals. With the aid of simulation, the company can establish ceilings and targets in the various investment classes and can describe in detail the screens or policies to be used to make choices in each of them. This will enable managers and staff personnel to understand management's objectives and to develop more appropriate and promising investment alternatives.

Using the same approach, executives can now examine in detail the kinds of investment opportunities generated by various segments of their businesses and select investment policies that will give them firmer control over their long-term growth. Top executives can analyze their own prejudices and test out the projected effects of inconsistent and irrational choices on their companies' long-term financial results. In short, top management can get back in the driver's seat and take charge of the most important element of the corporate future: effective investment for growth.

CHAPTER 7

Production-Distribution-Marketing Analysis

*A*S we have seen, a major capital investment usually implies an interlocking, uncertain structure of future revenues and costs. Analysis of companies' production-distribution-marketing activities in terms of interlocking systems has become a powerful competitive tool that is increasingly used by management to make sure that risks and returns remain as fully under control as possible. Application of management science methods in this operating area gives company executives increasing control over operating tactics and strategies, much as risk analysis gives management more control over the choice of investment projects and long-range plans. Analytical models of the total system for production, distribution, and marketing serve to improve the decisions that management makes to develop new markets and to meet stiffer competition, growing product-line complexity, and rising costs; in short, models help management to meet the chief challenges of today's fast-changing business environment.

A major advantage of systems analysis is that it enables management to better predict the effects of proposed actions throughout the interrelated parts of the company, and to do so without having to undergo the risks of actually taking these actions. Combinations of proposed improvements can also be tried and their potential results evaluated. Further refinements and alternatives can be tested after action has been taken. The potential impact of competitors' current or future market actions can likewise be used as input variables in an analytical model, and countermeasures can be developed, tested, and retested. The opportunities thus opened for managers are obviously limited only by the individual's needs and imagination.

EXAMPLES OF PROGRESS

Many companies have been using advanced management science models to deal with certain aspects of their operating problems. In logistics, for example, a number of companies have introduced systems to control field inventory, while others have developed models for improved production scheduling and control. Where companies have combined these systems well, effective total inventory control has been possible. But many companies have not yet completed this integration step.

As a further example, in distribution, companies have developed models to determine the optimum pattern of warehouses. This usually means establishing the optimum number and best location of distribution outlets to provide a selected level of customer service at minimum distribution and warehousing costs. Many successful models and algorithms have been used to improve the geographic patterns of warehouse location.

In purchasing, manufacturers have developed comprehensive ordering programs that continually project the needs for parts, update safety-stock requirements, and prepare detailed supply orders. As a requirement arises, a release is sent to a vendor identifying the quantity to be shipped; one truck and automobile manufacturer also includes the date that the parts should arrive at the factory. By specifying both quantity and date of delivery, the manufacturer has maintained a flow of parts (which in this case is worth close to $1 million per day) to meet production requirements and, at the same time, has reduced his own inventory levels. In effect, he is requiring the vendor to maintain an equitable inventory. Because trucks and automobiles have many parts, this program is lengthy and complex; in fact, it took three years to develop. However, other purchasing programs used by companies assembling less complicated products have produced similar benefits with commensurately less systems effort.

Finally, automobile and aerospace companies are now using critical path methods to control the design and introduction of new models. Critical path methods were first introduced in 1957 and used in the planning of military systems in the form of the PERT approach for the Navy's Polaris Weapon Systems in 1958 and have since been widely extended for use in business. These methods involve the detailed determination and controlled scheduling (by start and finish dates) of all of the interrelated activities that must precede the completion of a total project. Any activity that would delay the final finish date is "on the critical path." Hence the name.

Leading companies have put all these pieces together. In other words, although successful applications in the past have solved pieces of manufacturing and logistics problems, not many systems provided an *overall* management tool for planning and controlling costs and performance. The best systems models today coordinate the functional areas of logistics, production, and marketing. The best models also integrate planning and control across time by including the analysis of past results, control of present actions, and inputs for planning future changes.

For example, one leading company has designed an overall information system that provides coordinated planning and control for production, distribution (logistics), and marketing. At the heart of the system are two logistics models. The first of these models provides a means for determining the optimum number and locations of the company's warehouses. The second logistics model identifies the best mode for shipping directly from production to distribution outlets. In addition to these key models, an inventory replenishment procedure for warehouse stocks is included. The system also provides a production planning model, which is combined with the output of the logistics models and the replenishment procedure to determine the best levels of inventories for the individual warehouses. The production planning model simulates the flow of items from the production lines to the major distribution outlets and is used to determine (1) equipment schedules, (2) the best levels of manpower to provide a smooth operation preventing extreme hire and fire costs, and (3) the best pattern for seasonal inventory buildup to minimize costs of production and inventory.

At the other end of the spectrum, the system includes marketing models that are related to the logistics models to determine the optimum warehouse sources for a given distribution of customers and to establish the best schedules for local customer delivery. The key link with marketing factors is delivery reliability and cycle of customer service against orders.

Developing this integrated system of models and programming them for a computer was no small task for this company. To put it together, they first isolated the pieces, which in fact were beginnings in logistics and production, and then found the best methods, models, and procedures for tying them together. The end result is a workable system that provides coordinated planning and control across the functional areas of production, logistics, and marketing. The detailed development of this model and its use of the linear programming algorithm will be described later in this chapter. But first, it may be useful to examine another kind of distribution planning model that illustrates the broad scope of management science application.

A chemical company that operates an extensive railroad tank-car fleet designed a complete planning and control system for the rail distribution of its products. The system coordinates: the analysis of past results, day-to-day control of cars, and planning for changes in the total number and type of cars. This system has saved the company money directly, by enabling it to reduce its fleet of tank cars. In addition, however, the system has increased profits realized through marketing and production by improving customer service, either reducing intracompany deliveries or making them more efficient, and making tank cars available for holding inventory.

Figure 7-1 shows schematically how the system operates. A pool

Developing a Coordinated Information System

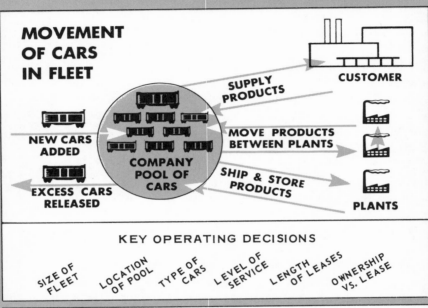

MOVEMENT OF CARS IN FLEET

NEW CARS ADDED

EXCESS CARS RELEASED

COMPANY POOL OF CARS

SUPPLY PRODUCTS

MOVE PRODUCTS BETWEEN PLANTS

SHIP & STORE PRODUCTS

CUSTOMER

PLANTS

KEY OPERATING DECISIONS

SIZE OF FLEET — LOCATION OF POOL — TYPE OF CARS — LEVEL OF SERVICE — LENGTH OF LEASES — OWNERSHIP VS. LEASE

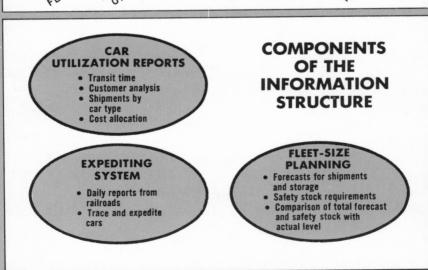

COMPONENTS OF THE INFORMATION STRUCTURE

CAR UTILIZATION REPORTS
- Transit time
- Customer analysis
- Shipments by car type
- Cost allocation

EXPEDITING SYSTEM
- Daily reports from railroads
- Trace and expedite cars

FLEET-SIZE PLANNING
- Forecasts for shipments and storage
- Safety stock requirements
- Comparison of total forecast and safety stock with actual level

FIGURE 7-1

of available cars of each type is used for three purposes: to supply products to customers, to move products between plants, and to ship and store products at the plant. After the tank car has delivered its load, it returns to the available pool of cars in the factory. From time to time, new cars are added and excess cars are released.

In management science terms, this fleet operation can be represented as an example of the general "waiting line" or "service queue" problem. A "waiting line" exists when cars are available in the plant; cars leave the line when they are in transit to customers or within plants. The problem is to determine the minimum number of cars that should be in the fleet to meet the patterns for each type of product and customer delivery requirement; that is, to assure that cars will always be available when needed. To provide analysis of results, control of day-to-day operations, and planning for future fleet sizes, this company developed a composite information system. Three components make up the system: one for preparing the car utilization reports, another for expediting both empty and full cars, and a third for fleet size planning.

Past results are handled in the system by car utilization reports that analyze transit times and identify the costs of serving customers. In addition, the component develops a tank-car distribution account monthly to provide the basis for allocating costs to profit centers. Furthermore, the reports show net sales (used to identify low-profit customers), and other reports provide product and volume analyses (used to identify opportunities to change the location of production and mode of shipment, and to reduce freight costs).

To control present results, the railcar expediting system develops and posts daily shipment records taken from railroad reportings of the actual locations of individual tank cars. This then permits tracing and expediting of cars delayed in national transit and follow-up on cars held by customers for long periods. The success of this portion of the system depends on the *daily* railroad reporting of tank-car location—a function rapidly being improved through the recent introduction by the Association of American Railroads of an all-inclusive information network. The major benefit of the expediting portion is that it allows management to concentrate on expediting those cars that are urgently needed at the factory and those that appear to have been lost in transit or at customer locations.

The final element of the system is the key to significant profit improvement: it permits fleet-size planning and indicates when cars should be added or released. This fleet-sizing program carries out the following steps:

- Forecasts tank-car needs for shipment and storage
- Translates forecasts into car requirements by type and size
- Calculates safety stock
- Compares total forecast and safety stock requirements to the actual level on hand

The decision rules for adding or releasing cars from the fleet were developed by simulation techniques similar to those used in risk analysis. In Figure 7-2, we see a typical result showing the number of cars needed to meet a given performance level.

For example, if certain requirements (for product, customers, etc.) call for twenty cars on the average, the company will need thirty-two cars in total (twelve additional) in the fleet to meet a performance of 99 percent availability of cars when required. If these same average requirements call for two cars, the fleet must have three more cars (a total of five) to meet the 99 percent level.

These examples illustrate how leading companies are linking their computer-based information systems to coordinated, company-wide systems in order to better operate their businesses. The comprehensive systems that result have two important features. They provide integration across functional lines, and they do a better job of integrating present status with future requirements in the areas of planning and control.

COMPLETE DEVELOPMENT OF A COORDINATED SYSTEM

In the rest of this chapter, the development of a coordinated planning and control system for production-distribution-marketing functions from scratch (rather than by linking partial systems already in existence) is described in detail. Many companies have not yet built operating and control systems for these separate functions and thus can now create a system to encompass the overall marketing, production, and distribution operations.

The description should enable readers to visualize what a comprehensive system analysis entails and to map out the major con-

Typical Results of Simulations

**NUMBER OF ADDITIONAL CARS NEEDED
TO MEET GIVEN PERFORMANCE LEVEL**

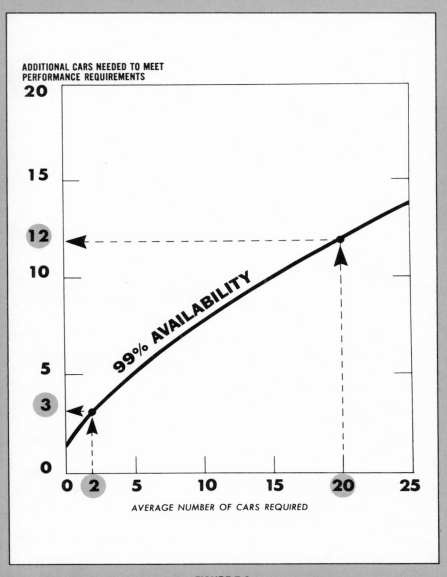

FIGURE 7-2

siderations relating to the development of similar approaches. Understanding the underlying logic of systems analysis should prove helpful in improving decision-making procedures, even in companies where the approach is not directly used to develop a model.

The application described covers the full-scale development of a production-distribution-marketing model for a typical large consumer goods company. The study leading to this model or coordinated system was intended to provide profitable answers to a set of specific questions; the model and its resulting information outputs are intended for continuing use by company management.

OBJECTIVES OF THE SYSTEMS ANALYSIS

The operating divisions of the company we shall be discussing serve approximately 7,000 customers and have annual sales of over $200 million. They manufacture several hundred products and distribute them through a system of multiple plants and warehouses.

The broad objective of the systems analysis was to assist management in making the most profitable use of its resources—human and physical. The work was partly oriented toward developing decisions for early profit improvement. The emphasis, however, was placed on developing a continuing, systematic program for the identification and exploitation of new manufacturing, distribution, and marketing profit opportunities. In particular, the results emphasized developing means for planning activities and making longer-term decisions under potential future conditions.

Improvements in profits, through short-term improvements in manufacturing and distribution operations, realized substantial initial savings of several million dollars a year. Moreover, powerful new management tools to support further improvements over the long term were developed during the study. These tools, which integrated technical management science methods with the company's basic information systems, included:

1. A mathematical model of the company's production-distribution-marketing system
2. A file of operating and selling cost data

3. A demand data model characterizing customers, their demands, and the individual selling divisions

Assembling data needed for the models presented problems typical of such approaches. These problems, along with the complexity of the analytical tools, determined both the extent and importance of the necessary computer programming effort.

The production-distribution system model is illustrated by a flow chart (Figure 7-3). Linear programming is used to determine the best allocation or assignment in each of its three stages: to establish warehouse service areas for meeting customer demand in regional markets (Stage 1: the distribution stage); to set annual plant production assignments to meet warehouse needs (Stage 2: annual production assignment stage); and to specify monthly production plans (Stage 3). As the diagram indicates, each of the three linear programs operating upon the information inputs shown (e.g., freight and warehouse costs) produces an allocation or assignment result that is fed into the next stage, along with additional costs and other information necessary to produce the next result. Because the result of each stage affects a cost that is used in the preceding stage, the model run is repeated using the newly determined costs from the following stage until an optimum equilibrium condition among all three stages is reached.[1]

HOW THE WORK WAS DONE

The first task in the study was to develop a work plan that carefully defined the study's objectives, the problem areas to be covered, the methods and procedures to be followed, and the major questions to be answered. Refined and modified during the course of the work, the plan played a central role in bringing this long-term project to successful completion and in keeping all the project's phases oriented toward the stated objectives.

Because of the scope and duration of this analysis, its successful conclusion was significantly aided by the use of teams. An invaluable secondary benefit of using the team approach was that it effec-

---

[1] Theoretically, with large enough computers, only one linear programming stage would be required. Because this was a full-scale, practical situation, the size (4,000 equations) was then too large for a single-stage linear program to be practical. Therefore, three stages were used.

The Production and Distribution System Model Flow Chart

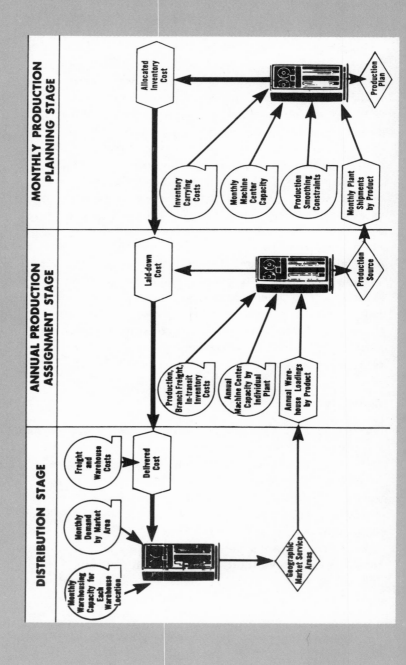

tively trained key company executives to continue exploiting the type of management science tools used in the study.

The basic study team was a Steering Committee, a group of vice-presidents whose close cooperation was important in the development of the study plan. In addition, this team was responsible for overall administration of the study and for review of recommendations. The vice-president–controller was given the detailed responsibilities of administering the work.

Four working teams were organized under the vice-president–controller:

1. *A Managment Policies Team,* which provided definitions of company policies and statements of proposed procedures. This group also helped develop and review the work plan.

2. *A Product Demand Team,* whose main purpose was to review, analyze, and explain marketing operations and the interaction between company and customer.

3. *A Production and Distribution Team,* which provided data on the production and distribution system, and reviewed and analyzed its operations.

4. *A Model-building Team,* which had major responsibility for assembling data for the model of the system and helped develop the model.

The work of these teams, especially the data assembly work, was supplemented by supporting staffs from time to time. Except for the Model-building Team, which worked full time throughout the study, the teams were involved only part time, working only during certain phases of data collection and report preparation or review.

Full-time administration of the study was handled for the controller by a management science study manager. Because of the time and talents required, the computer programming was done by an outside programming organization.

Linear programming's role

Linear programming (LP), as we have noted, can be viewed both as a model and algorithm for finding the most profitable combinations of activities to accomplish a desired end result. A brief review of LP will indicate how it played an essential role in this particular project and will also indicate that it has many other key applications. Indeed, LP is one of the pillars of management science, underlying much of today's understanding of methods for improved decision making.

In 1945, Dr. George Stigler, then an economics professor at Columbia, wrote a pioneering article on LP entitled "The Cost of Subsistence." His work illustrated the principles of LP, foreshadowing it as a breakthrough in the application of science to management. Not long thereafter it was recognized as being applicable to the complexities of production-marketing-distribution systems.

Stigler was trying to find out which of seventy-seven foods would provide a satisfactory minimum balance of nine nutrients (calories, proteins, calcium, iron, vitamin A, thiamine, riboflavin, niacin, and ascorbic acid) at minimum cost. He wrote a series of straightforward equations (they would hold no terrors for a high school algebra student) stating exactly what conditions had to be met; how each possible ingredient of the diet contributed, per unit of weight, to those conditions; and what the cost of any ingredient was per unit of weight.

By solving those equations, Stigler found that at 1944 prices the optimum diet (not considering variety or palatableness—which might, of course, be built into similar equations) would have consisted principally of wheat, flour, cabbage, and hog liver, and for one person would have cost $59.88 for the year.

The same kind of "linear programming" equations apply importantly to production and distribution problems in industry (as well as to many other kinds of management problems). For example, suppose that a company producing a range of products wants to optimize profits, using the equipment it has available. The problem posed for management is to determine which products and how much of each to produce in order to maximize the company's profits.[2]

If the costs of raw materials, the selling price, and the capacity required on each type of equipment are known for every product, a series of equations can be written describing the drain on the

---

[2] Existing practice in many cases is to produce those products with the highest direct profit margin. Because of the interrelationship of available machine capacities with *total* profitability, it can be shown that, in general, this practice leads to profits lower than the maximum possible.

available equipment and the profit generated by each of the products. These equations, along with others detailing the available capacity for each type of equipment, form the basis for an LP solution.

In essence, the optimum solution is developed by determining through successive steps the net incomes yielded by each of the various products as they are added to or subtracted from the combination without violating the restraints of capacity. Then the mathematical rules of LP are applied in repeated cycles to find increasingly profitable combinations of products to put through the system. Because of the rigorous mathematical algorithm,[3] each cycle gives a better profitability result, and the last cycle identifies the combination making the maximum possible contribution to profits. The yields of any other combinations can then be precisely compared with the optimum one and with one another. Further, the values of relieving the restraints on productive capacity are indicated directly by the solution.

Linear programming analyses of this kind frequently take prices as constants and pursue the search for maximum profitability and relative profitabilities in terms of least-cost and lesser-cost combinations of production and distribution facilities. This was the case in the study described here as an example. The model and the programs expressed the operating costs and capabilities of the entire production, distribution, and marketing system of the company's operating divisions. One important objective of the study was to find the least-cost way of satisfying customer demand, considering the interactions of all the factors involved.

In view of the size and complexity of the full-scale analysis, a simplified version, or prototype (used before the final programming of the model to test the model and to illustrate its use), is diagramed in Figure 7-4. This prototype, a small-scale version of the full model, incorporates special characteristics of the actual situation, such as warehouses—at plant locations and elsewhere —or specialized machines located only at certain plants. Note that the two plants manufacture on four types of machines and deliver five products (one purchased) to three warehouses (which in turn deliver to ten market areas). This prototype is small enough

---

[3] The basic algorithm is the Simplex method, developed by George Dantzig in 1949.

The Prototype Production Distribution System

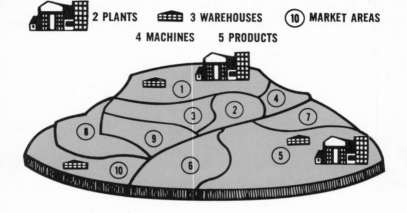

2 PLANTS · 3 WAREHOUSES · ⑩ MARKET AREAS
4 MACHINES · 5 PRODUCTS

Prototype Analysis

AVERAGE ANNUAL SOLUTION

The Market Areas are assigned by the linear program to warehouses to:

- Satisfy demand
- Observe constraints and limitations including warehouse throughput capacities by months
- Minimize total customer shipping charges and warehouse costs

OPTIMUM ASSIGNMENT OF MARKET AREAS TO WAREHOUSE SERVICE AREAS

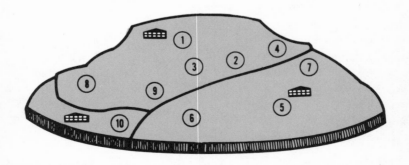

FIGURE 7-4

to allow quick and easy calculation of solutions in checking the validity of the mathematical formulation and the solution procedures.

Examination of how the prototype worked will illustrate how linear programming can assist management in tackling similar problems. First consider Market Area 4 (Figure 7-4) and the model's Stage 1 (the warehouse-to-customer distribution stage) analyses. Market Area 4 had the following monthly demand (in pounds) of different prototype company products.

Monthly Product Demand in Market Area 4

Product	Monthly demand (pounds)
1	68
2	2,238
3	8,280
4	30,799
5	2,545
	43,930

A first cut (Stage 1 analysis) with the prototype took the average customer freight costs for shipping to Market Area 4 as: 5.70 cents per pound from Warehouse 1; 4.32 cents per pound from W are-house 2; and 7.99 cents per pound from Warehouse 3. (In estao-lishing total customer freights costs, the full model considered the product class and weight for each shipment, rather than the average freight rates used here.) With these average customer freight costs, the least expense for serving Market Area 4 would be realized by shipping from Warehouse 2: Warehouse 2's total charge would be $1,893, versus $2,500 for Warehouse 1 and $3,500 for Warehouse 3.

Freight cost, however, was not the only factor to consider in defining the most economical service areas for each warehouse. The monthly throughput capacity of each warehouse was also critical. Monthly assignments to each warehouse clearly must be no greater than the capacity of that warehouse to handle the goods. As a result, assignments that might have been ideal for each market area individually might not have been feasible for the system as a whole. To determine a feasible least-cost delivery assignment schedule, management used an LP model to consider the interactions among the market areas in their competing demands for the limited throughput capacity of each possible warehouse. The solution that was reached when this approach was tested with the prototype model appears in Figure 7-4, which shows the optimum assignment of market areas to warehouse service areas.

With the configuration of service areas determined in the prototype test solution, the total annual cost of the system would be $180,363. As can be seen, this solution did result in the assignment of Market Area 4 to the territory of Warehouse 2, the warehouse from which freight costs were lowest for Market Area 4. However, market areas were not assigned to warehouse territories on the basis of freight costs alone; capacities of plants were also considered. For example, Market Area 6 was assigned in the test solution to Warehouse 1, although the cheaper freight-cost assignment for Area 6 would have been to Warehouse 3.

This part of the analysis illustrates a very important feature of LP models, namely, their ability to determine the cost impact of alternatives precisely and economically. For instance, further analysis with the prototype showed that the shift of Market Area 6 to Warehouse 3 would additionally save annual distribution costs of $674 but at the expense of a required 2 percent increase in the throughput capacity of Warehouse 3. Or, for a different illustration, suppose that special regional sales considerations had indicated that Market Areas 2 and 4 should be assigned to Warehouse 1 rather than to Warehouse 2. The prototype linear program showed this switch to be feasible from the standpoint of throughput capacities but also showed that the shift would incur annual costs nearly $14,000 over those for the optimum solution. In consequence, management might reason that, if such a shift were made, the marketing advantage should generate savings or net revenues of at least $14,000 in return.

Now, how can these systems models help management approach broader problems of marketing policy? For example, suppose a company wished to examine alternative policies on minimum order sizes. Minimum order size is certainly related to order frequency. Policies on minimum order sizes would consequently have an impact on costs such as customer freight, traffic services, warehousing and shipping, and sales order services. If an analysis of the data files is used along with the distribution model, both the net cost and the operating impact of alternative minimum-order-size policies can be evaluated, and the policy that would result in optimum profits can be determined. This evaluation of the cost and profit impact of each possible alternative policy and the determination of the optimum-profit policy were carried out through linear programming. Among other policy areas analyzed were product manufacturing assignments, returned goods policies, and shipment pooling. Alternatives for each policy area were assessed in the light of data on production costs and capacities, and so on. Market characteristics, operations characteristics, and related variable costs are examples of the major types of data drawn on in the analyses.

The linear programming analysis arrived at solutions to problems within the total production-distribution-marketing systems that reflected all relevant costs on an integrated basis. It did so as follows, proceeding cyclically through the model's three stages: first, distribution assignments of warehouses to customers (by monthly periods); second, annual assignments of shipments from plant to warehouse; and third, monthly production planning assignments for plants. For the analyses, the nationwide market was divided into 300 market areas, approximately uniform with respect to demographic features. Limitations that were taken into account included production-smoothing requirements (to realize stable employment levels), monthly machine-center capacities, and inventory carrying costs at the plant. Stage 3 determined the quantity of each product to be produced monthly at each plant, i.e., a complete monthly production plan. At this stage, the inventory costs for the selection-production schedule could be determined and fed back to Stage 1, to allow for rerunning the model on the computer until minimum cost equilibrium was reached.

MAKING THE ANALYSIS PAY OFF

The payoff of such a study comes when the initial results of the analyses can be applied fully and management can use its new tools on a continuing and profitable basis. There are four phases in all such undertakings. They constitute the preparation and implementation needed to apply management science methods profitably in the analysis of production-distribution-marketing systems. Subsequent work may, of course, improve profits further and will demonstrate whether management has gained merely a set of valuable findings or has developed a whole new capability for increasing profits.

In the first phase, an extremely important one, a study plan should be developed that tentatively specifies the most sensitive operating and marketing areas in the system. These areas should then be examined for possible immediate improvements. When, in a later phase, the various models have been developed, these areas should be analyzed in more depth to provide the necessary understanding of the intricacies, complexities, and interactions of the system.

In the second major phase, working teams should be set up and rough-cut analyses of selected policies and procedures should be made. In addition, the ultimate production and distribution model should be outlined. Finally, data requirements must be specified and a detailed data collection program initiated.

In the third major phase, which may overlap much of the second phase, preparation for final analyses should be made. Perhaps a prototype model can now be developed and tested, using realistic data. This will make it possible to test the bases of a large model and to illustrate and explain the model to management before full-scale programming begins. Computer programs for assembly of the raw data, data analyses, and the final model should be completed during this third phase.

The fourth major phase involves actual performance of the analyses and development of recommendations. The recommendations should establish optimum assignments, policies, and procedures for the areas selected for investigation. The final results are then worked out with management and an implementation program is developed.

The details of these phases illustrate typical features of soundly conducted management science efforts. In the illustrative case, the rough-cut analyses of selected policies and procedures of the second phase, for example, eliminated lengthy later study by reaching the following conclusions:

- Changes in quantity-discount pricing do not have sufficient system-wide potential to warrant further consideration.
- Drop-shipment allowances should be left unchanged for the

time being because the net differential in cost is small between shipments to dealer stock and drop shipments—considering the attention the dealers give to the whole product line.

■ Returned-goods policies should be revised; preliminary analysis of them should suggest specific changes.

■ Changing the amount of direct selling to small accounts could result in significant cost savings.

■ Regulation of minimum order size could offer significant cost-savings because the then current policy framework permitted numerous exceptions, which indicated that it needed study.

In the fourth and last phase, the full set of analytical tools and assembled data were applied to all the policy issues to be investigated. First, the data and findings developed in the previous phases were drawn on to identify the characteristics and operations associated with each policy. Then the full model was used to determine the total cost under current and alternative policies for the policy issue being explored. The analysis for each policy issue began with the specification of optimum warehouse service area and optimum production assignments. Evaluation of the particular policy issue thus reflected the characteristics of that issue alone, without taking into account the economics of changed service area and production assignments. This gave management a basis for evaluating the incremental profitability of alternative policies.

For example, the model determined the annual system-wide saving that would result from the setting of minimum order sizes by various proposed new policies (e.g., there would be savings of about $176,000 with a minimum order size equivalent to 100 pounds).

Other policies that were examined included:

■ Realignment of warehouse service area and production assignments

■ Institution of quantity discount pricing for truckload orders

■ Change in drop-shipment allowances

■ Restriction of acceptance of returned goods

■ Reduction in the amount of direct selling to small accounts

■ Reduction in special handling of back orders

■ Restriction of the frequency of shipping to single customers

■ Refusal to accept split-case orders

■ Decrease of the volume of less-than-truckload shipments through pooling

■ Liberalization of the plant-to-warehouse assignment restrictions

Thus, these linear programming and data analysis models enable management to constantly examine its policies and decisions in terms of the total production-distribution system. The outputs of the models also provide a basis for understanding many aspects of the business that previously had been difficult to evaluate. For example, in order to be able to service less profitable ship-to locations through such channels as wholesalers rather than by direct selling, the company wanted to determine the profitability of the 6,300 ship-to locations that realized less than \$2,000 in annual sales. Accordingly, the company devised a means for determining the profitability of any specified account, evaluating that profitability against some standard, determining the causes of divergence, and adopting an appropriate plan of action. The cost information was obtained directly from the data and analyses generated by the linear programming. Such data provide management with information of a kind and quality not previously available.

As we saw in Chapter 1, linear programming is extremely versatile in determining least-cost, maximum-profit solutions to resource allocation problems of many kinds. This example suggests the power, range, and flexibility of the LP technique in individual applications. Executives need to understand when and how LP can be used to advantage and what kinds of valuable results it can produce. Linear programming can be applied to any allocation problem in which costs and returns vary in at least an approximately linear manner; that is, in proportion to such elements as quantities, distances, or times. This is essentially the case in a great many business operations.[4]

MAKING PROFITABLE USE OF LP

The effective and profitable use of LP depends largely upon data collection and computer programming. Guidelines for carrying out these tasks include the following:

[4] Many nonlinear situations can be structured as LPs. Unsophisticated LP applications, which do not take into account complex business considerations, will yield only the optimum solution and eliminate all near optimum solutions unless special care is taken to retrieve them. However, this need not seriously concern an executive if he is working with capable management science specialists.

Specify the data system early in an analysis. For example, in the illustrative case, a key factor was the ability to make marketing and distribution decisions responsive to detailed variation in customer requirements from area to area throughout the country.[5] In addition, the area selected at the outset for detailed analysis required comprehensive data on customer demands and transactions. Thus, a "complete enumeration" philosophy was adopted; i.e., the data system was designed to represent the actual marketing operation, to characterize the individual selling divisions, and to provide the data required for each sale as precisely as possible. In addition, however, it was designed from the beginning to promote analytical flexibility; because it was intended to be a process for long-term continuing application, the uses of the data were expected to grow.

Under the complete-enumeration philosophy, the file of demand data was made compatible with the company's sales statistics program; in this way wasteful duplication of basic data was avoided.

Look for possible problem areas and roadblocks from the beginning. For example, the production-distribution-marketing model used in this analysis required detailed specification of customer activity by region. This entailed two significant problems: first, designating invoice ship-to versus bill-to locations; second, determining shipment freight charges. Detailed matching of freight bills with invoices was not feasible, so a freight-costing model was developed to generate the freight charges applicable to each shipment. If such problems are identified early, it is possible to organize immediately for the data collection and programming operations that will be necessary to solve them. Where such data are of continuing use and require updating, provision should be made for generating them as part of regular accounting procedures in the future.

Segment the data files and programs so they can be revised easily and used selectively. For example, different data may be needed for a production-distribution-marketing model, for studies of policies and procedures, for characterization of the selling divisions, and for development of sales statistics. Because such analyses place varied demands on files and programs, it may be necessary to main-

---

[5] For analytical purposes, it will be recalled, the country had been divided into 300 market areas, ranging from major metropolitan centers to rural regions.

tain generalized files. For this company, generalized files consisted of a detailed record of invoice and shipment statistics. (The overall plan should take into account the fact that in every special and future project some additional programming must be done to get the data in the detailed form required.)

Segment the computer programming. For production-distribution-marketing models, the individual computer programs are usually significantly interrelated. Even so, it is not necessary to prepare these individual programs sequentially. When a number of such programs are to be created, the overall time requirements can be reduced by planning them like a large-scale project—i.e., breaking it up into segments, without losing sight of construction areas of interdependence. With input and output formats for major program segments specified at an early stage, the programming work can be allocated among a number of programmers. Of course, it will be necessary for the technical specialists on the project to review the individual programs and arbitrate any issues that may arise.

REALIZING THE PAYOUT

Finally, here are a few general guides to ensuring full payout from the use of management science tools in production-distribution-marketing problems.

First, the comprehensive model should not demand a level of detail in the input that would make adequate forecasting impossible.

Second, it is important to identify tasks and responsibilities and set up timetables. In the illustrative study, formal provision was made for twice-a-month automatic review by the Steering Committee of the status of all projects. These reviews kept the committee aware of progress; through the reviews, new timetables were developed at adequate levels of authority, and authorization was obtained as warranted for additional personnel or other variations from the original plans.

Third, it is important to be alert to new opportunities for applying the models being developed. Nothing ensures continued interest and use of the basic models developed in a management science effort more than the successful development of applications to current problems of management concern. To ensure that new applications of the models will be identified, management must learn what the models can do and must develop and continue close communication with specialists.

Fourth, it is a good idea to get early agreement on computer outputs that will help management evaluate the results of model runs and to plan implementation.

Fifth, it is necessary to establish organizational arrangements to implement project results and to generate, evaluate, and work on new projects.

SUMMARY

Models concretely representing a company's combined production-distribution-marketing functions can serve as powerful management tools. Tested ways of building comprehensive models of this kind and related analytic procedures and algorithms have proven fully practical. With such models, the managers of a company can project in advance the probable results of proposed major manufacturing and distribution moves across the full range of the company's production activities and markets. Models that handle financial data provide representations of any significant accounting relations. Such models can integrate variable cost data into the accounting system, to support profitability accounting and flexible budget structures. The most profitable plans for any functional area of the business can thus be developed through successive tests. Such capability in a firm that is well managed in other respects could make it unbeatable in its field.

CHAPTER 8
Building Better
Marketing Models

MANAGEMENT science methods have proved to be powerful marketing tools and now they take a major place in the repertoire of problem-solving techniques for this key component of modern business. These methods have been accomplishing more in marketing than most businessmen realize. This is mainly because the companies that have pioneered in the use of management science to improve marketing decision making have held the results "close to the vest" to protect their competitive advantages.

One company, for instance, has used management science to achieve savings of several million dollars in advertising expense with no loss in advertising effectiveness. To do so, this leading consumer packaged-goods company developed a series of mathematical models. It first constructed a computer program using one of the now well-known media selection models.[1] Then, it evaluated the relative impact and benefit-cost ratios of various media and, finally, extended the media model to develop alternative total advertising budgets. The budget provided for allocations—based on analyses of marginal cost for reaching various audiences—by geographic market and by product.

Other companies, including du Pont, General Motors, U.S. Steel, Westinghouse, General Foods, and Bristol-Myers, are using these types of approaches to project potential market conditions and product-line sales five to ten years ahead. Many organizations are developing computer-based models to provide insights into the relationships of sales, marketing, promotion, advertising, packaging, and competitive activity as they affect profits. The models, generally, depend upon data inputs derived from all elements of the companies' activity and experience.[2]

To experiment with the influence of varying advertising levels on net profits, one company selling a consumer product developed an advertising model combining historical data with judgmental inputs about the next year's economic climate, competitive product, and advertising decisions. So that the advertising and market research programs could be developed directly from the data needs as revealed by the model, a computer terminal—to be used by advertising management—was placed in the advertising department.

MANAGEMENT SCIENCE SOLUTIONS TO BASIC MARKETING PROBLEMS

The usefulness of sophisticated techniques in organizing the vast amount of data that is required to plan efficient advertising programs is now widely recognized, and the use of these techniques has become fairly commonplace. Management science methods

---

[1] Various versions of media selection computer routines are available and are used by most advertising agencies. These models help choose media schedules, given required judgmental inputs as to effectiveness and other data, to meet a specified cost or coverage objective.

[2] *The Gallagher Report*, vol. XVI, no. 25, New York, June 18, 1968, provides a brief, broadly based description of what a number of companies are doing with the management sciences in marketing and sales.

are, however, being successfully applied on a broader scale to find answers to many basic marketing problems. Here are some examples of the many approaches to these problems—approaches that have been made possible by management science techniques.

Product-line planning. "How should the product line be planned to take advantage of market penetration, production capabilities, and delivery and service facilities? How can the potential needs of a regional or worldwide group of customers best be served?"

One clothing manufacturer worked out a method for finding the optimum number of styles and colors for his product line. The chief objective, of course, was first to provide a product base large enough to attract customers to the entire line and then to gain their exclusive patronage for each individual product item. Against this objective, the company had to weigh the added costs of greater variety: both the obvious direct expenses and such hidden costs as the reduced efficiency of salesmen dealing with an increased number of models. It was very much in the company's interest to add items to the line as long as they caused net sales and net profits to increase. But it was just as vital not to add so many items that profits would be depressed. When a model was developed to analyze the data, it was found that incremental sales of added items showed a remarkably stable pattern over the years. There was also a clear relationship between these sales and related costs. Thus, the number of products to be offered in given lines could be set at the optimum profit level.

Product-line analysis similarly benefited a producer in another field altogether—a major component division of an electronics firm. The company prepared a computer-based model to describe the movement of its products through manufacturing and distribution and to indicate the costs connected with every step. Customer sales information at every inventory stage from factory to distributor was incorporated into the model. After analyzing inventories and costs, in terms of demand, the division found that it could cut the number of product types by 20 percent and total inventories by 30 percent, without significant reduction in sales or service, thereby substantially improving its profits.

Sales forecasts. "How can market potentials be forecast for wide ranges of products, and how can the uncertainties of competition best be estimated for each product area?"

Some of the many advanced forecasting techniques now in use project prices and demand for a company's products in the light of such factors as economic cycles and industry inventory levels and turnover rates. Use of techniques such as "exponential smoothing" —which minimizes forecasting error by systematically weighing seasonal factors and irregularly high or low past results—has become so widespread that various computer manufacturers and software firms offer standard programs to implement this forecasting method.

Years of intensive and continuing research have realized outstanding results for the Anheuser-Busch brewing concern. With its highly developed forecasting and analytic system, Anheuser-Busch was able several years ago to predict its market share for each sales territory with great accuracy. It could estimate in advance what profit would be realized from any given level of advertising budget. This, in turn, enabled it to find the optimum advertising level, market by market. Finally, it could determine the minimum advertising budget it needed, market by market as well as nationally, to reach a specified profit goal. As a result, it consistently increased its share of the market.

Distribution systems. "How can the capacities and locations of distributing points be planned so as to deliver products to customers at minimum cost?"

Management science methods have been used so often and so successfully for problems of this type that they have become standard techniques. For example, a company had more than twenty field warehouses that had—typically—sprung up haphazardly over the years in response to accidents of volume and demography in individual sales territories rather than according to an overall plan. Management science analysis showed that the firm could save several million dollars a year by using a system made up of just eight of the old warehouses and two new ones, with much greater shipment of products direct from factories to customers. In addition, operating rules for the new distribution system permitted large reductions in inventory, while order filling was as prompt as before.

Customer service. "How can the most profitable level of customer service and the means to provide it be determined?"

One company that sold a rapidly growing line of office equipment needed to know how many field service personnel to add in each territory. Sales regularly increased, but so did the load of customers' maintenance and repair requirements. The problems differed widely in each territory, along with types and ages of machines, types of customer businesses, local travel and traffic conditions, and local customers' service expectations. A thorough analysis spotlighted patterns of service requirements for various kinds of users, travel times, and service times, using these patterns and other data as inputs. A computer simulation model determined the number of service personnel to be added at specific locations in order to provide local customers with varying levels of service. Typical findings involved in the solution are shown graphically in Figure 8-1. The results provided a tool with which company management could, according to its promotional and cost objectives in a given territory, vary its procedures to satisfy, for example, anywhere from a minimum number of customers (perhaps half) to a maximum number (perhaps almost all). One notable finding of the analysis was that a 5 percent increase in average customer satisfaction at midrange required a 25 percent increase in service cost. With these findings, the company was able to give predetermined service throughout the country, using local customer preferences and local conditions to determine the level of satisfaction delivered.

The same general method has proved equally effective for problems of customer delivery time in cases where prompt or timely deliveries are major customer considerations.

Pricing policies. "How should pricing policies and pricing strategies be set so as to optimize our long-range positions in various markets?"

To establish a pricing policy of maximum effectiveness, one company developed a computer simulation model that took into account the following factors: elasticity of demand, potential market shares under competitive retaliation, possible future price weaknesses, potential changes in costs (including such offsetting factors as greater service requirements and improved transportation efficiency), and changes in local market structures. The approach required two stages of model building and testing, the first for a single market and the second for all markets combined. The results enabled management to evaluate the expected payoffs for alternative price structures and to investigate the role of each

A Computer Model for Providing Customer Service

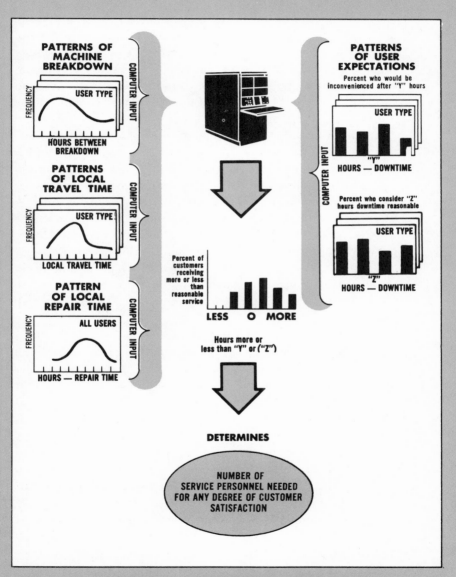

FIGURE 8-1

input factor in shaping the output results. Unlike traditional methods, with their once-and-for-all resolution, this approach provided a step-by-step analysis of alternatives that could be applied to future changed conditions and to long-term projections on an ongoing basis.

Again, a railroad company explored combined price and equipment policies to determine how its freight business would be affected by the introduction of special-purpose cars and commodity rates. An overall analysis of the effects on profits of seasonal factors and total usage led to the introduction of new rates and equipment, geared to the demand patterns most favorable for the railroad.

Another company that sold manufacturing services (essentially machine time) had to bargain constantly over prices in a highly competitive environment. It constantly had to weigh the advantages of a sure sale at a lower price against the possibility of being able to sell the same productive capacity later at a higher price. A historical analysis of the company's demand patterns was extended into the future from a specified base. The results were then incorporated in a system for calculating the probable market for specified capacity at a given moment and at a set price. The result enabled management to make day-by-day price decisions and to accurately estimate the profitability of prospective business at all times.

Best mix of sales, advertising, and promotion programs. "How should sales, advertising, and promotion efforts be allocated to various products so as to provide the optimum pattern of customer demand?"

One marketing leader initiated an extensive management science study of how expenditures could best be allocated among different elements of the marketing mix. It developed a model that helped point to the most effective way of obtaining data needed to test out field advertising and retail sales efforts and led to a decision to change the relative emphasis on advertising and on the retail merchandising force.

Another example is a consumer durable-goods manufacturer that wanted to know how much of the advertising and sales promotion budgets should be allocated to each product line in order to maximize its profits. The firm also sought an indication of the profitability of introducing a new, intermediate-priced line. The example thus suggests, incidentally, that management science often works most advantageously when used to solve a combination of problems rather than just one. In solving this combination of problems, management first constructed a profile of the market by price line and then projected it ten years into the future. Among other things, this step established that the entire market was declining and that the company's share was decreasing. Analysis of variables affecting these trends permitted identification of factors influencing market share, such as number of outlets and share of advertising expenditure, and also made it possible to identify the effect of price. A mathematical model was constructed to quantify the impact of these variables on the company's market share and profitability. Further work with the model showed that introduction of the medium-priced line would be to the company's advantage and defined how the advertising and sales promotion budgets should be allocated to each line for optimum profits.

Most effective overall management coordination. "How can the activities of the entire marketing, distribution, and manufacturing complex be tied together most strongly over the long run?"

Companies that have been engaged longest in developing management science systems for decision making in all their prime business areas have shown a strong tendency to coordinate these systems for maximum effect. These systems are necessarily interdependent. The output of one system is the input of another; sales results influence production, and both influence distribution; distribution, in turn, influences both sales and production; and all systems influence, and are influenced by, financial management. One company, for example, has a single, management science developed system that includes models for forecasting, sales planning, inventory planning, and production planning. These models give management a rigorous analytical basis for reaching decisions on such questions as adding or dropping products, introducing varieties of items in product lines, scheduling the company's plants (for assigning overall levels of operations as well as capacity for each product), producing inventories before selling seasons, purchasing raw materials, setting sales and advertising budgets, and improving manufacturing facilities by eliminating or introducing equipment.

Comprehensive coordinated systems like this are still exceptional in American business, but they will soon be the rule. Many businesses of all sizes are now developing such comprehensive systems. Larger organizations that have not started developing such systems may find it hard if not impossible to compete effectively in the future (this is particularly true in the marketing area). It should be noted, of course, that companies do not develop these overall systems as *one* integrated model; rather, as we have demonstrated, they attain them by coordinating models for several decision-problem areas.

THE DEMAND PATTERN IN MARKETING STRATEGY

Key factors underlying all marketing problems are the variations in product demand as functions of time and geography. The concept of "demand patterns" is a powerful tool of management science applied to marketing. A demand pattern may be defined as a description of the way point-of-sale transactions (that occur within a given time period—an hour, a day, a week, a year—in a given location or area, involving a particular type of buyer) vary. In aggregate, each company has as many demand patterns as there are possible combinations of such variables.

Two kinds of management science approaches to marketing problems are related to demand patterns:

1. Approaches that attempt to optimize the operating results from a given set of demand patterns. There are management science applications for this kind of problem, as we have seen, which usually involves shipping, inventories, and warehousing.

2. Approaches that seek to change the characteristics or parameters of one or more demand patterns. Here, the influence of various decisions on the behavior of buyers, wholesalers, and others must be dealt with.

Many critical marketing problems are of the second kind: problems of determining what factors influence the demand patterns (both intermediate and final) of the company's customers and of determining how the company can handle these factors to shape the future demand patterns that will be best suited to its resources and its interests. This type of marketing problem is receiving much management science attention today.

One current approach to this kind of problem is to develop a model of the market structure. Such a detailed corporate model indicates how the market is influenced by the variables controlled by the company and shows the interactions of these variables in the firm's operations. For example, the following interactions are typical of those the executive must take into account if he attempts to develop a strategy to influence demand patterns for the efficient long-term operation of his business. Suppose that the market in which company A performs is influenced by advertising and promotion (or sales effort), price, and service performance. In turn, service performance is influenced by service policy, which is controlled by cost and investment. Investment responds to the rate of return (which is the basic criterion for evaluating results), and rate of return is, in part, influenced by service policy through actual service performance. In turn, service performance is controlled by market share, which follows the derived demand and revenue flow.

In contrast to plant investments, which usually commit large amounts of capital for long periods of time, marketing investments (i.e., sales and service forces, advertising programs) are usually subject to much more precise control for shorter time periods. But if control is to be precise, the system used to sense and influence the environment must be capable of sensing the direction of the changes that these expenditures bring about in its business *and* of predicting the effect those changes will have on the operations of the marketing system. Marketing activities can be adapted to meet the challenges posed by continual change only when the marketing information system is adapted to the most effective decision time requirements, since marketing is, in effect, continuing experimentation in a many-variable laboratory. It is precisely this adaptive requirement that makes the understanding of demand patterns important.

Knowing the shape of its demand patterns enables a company to effectively solve problems of meeting customer demand—to be sensitive to significant changes in the customer environment and at the same time to develop mechanisms to test out means of changing the demand patterns to the company's advantage. For example, Figure 8-2 shows a group of typical demand patterns for a consumer product. Chronologically, one can start with the demand per day at a local warehouse (see "Daily demands at a local ware-

Typical Demand Patterns

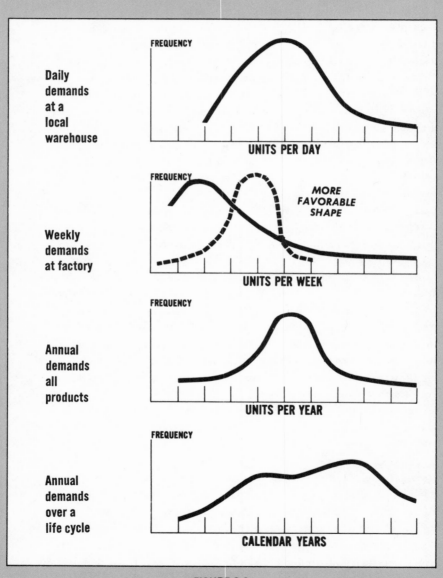

FIGURE 8-2

house," Figure 8-2). This curve provides information that will determine local inventory requirements, customer service, and order size.

Total demands at the factory for a particular week reflecting inventory requirements are shown in Figure 8-2 ("Weekly demands at factory"). More importantly, it suggests the possibility of changing the demand curve to a more favorable shape through the use of sales promotion, advertising, or sales force control. Similar curves can be developed for monthly patterns and for groups of products on a yearly basis. Thus, Figure 8-2 ("Annual demands all products") shows the spread of annual demand for the product line. The probable life cycle of the typical product also can be developed as shown in Figure 8-2 ("Annual demands over a life cycle"). These chronological, experience-based probability distributions usually differ geographically and demographically. Segmented by time, location, and population group, they describe the company's market. Changes in that market mean changes in at least one of these patterns. Changes in one pattern generally bring about changes in others.

Attempts to change the shape of these patterns—to raise the average sales per product, the total for a given product, or the lower end of the daily demand curve—have usually proved successful when investigators have first traced through the sequence of effects that the change might have on the entire marketing system.

When applied successfully to marketing problems, this management science approach generally demonstrates three advantages:

1. It can work from a wide array of facts and variables. It can measure the importance or sensitivity of the final outcome to marginal changes in either the assumptions or the decisions. It can point the way to a versatile solution of the problem, one that will work well over a wide range of assumptions—about market conditions, for example.

2. It begins to reveal explicitly the logical cause-and-effect relationships between the pieces in the marketing puzzle.

3. It specifically recognizes that combinations of events with differing probability patterns are basic to pricing and other marketing decisions. Guesses based simply on a single probable outcome frequently have unhappy consequences.

PROBLEMS AND CONSEQUENCES

Not all efforts to apply management science to marketing activities have been successful. Despite its vast potential in marketing applications, it has failed to solve marketing problems for each of these reasons at one time or another:

Lack of competent personnel. A high order of technical skill is required to deal with problems of decision making amid uncertainty. Second-order effects that change the shape of demand curves, as well as large numbers of variables, are also involved. In addition, the selection of methods and the development of adequate models require an intimate understanding of the physical and social processes of marketing. This understanding has often been lacking in unsuccessful studies.

Lack of sound data. There are always plenty of data available in marketing problems, but often they are not of the right kind. If research is inadequate, information on cause-and-effect relationships will be insufficient. Selection of data is especially difficult because of the uncertainty involved in marketing problems. Some key relationships—relative effectiveness of different advertising media, for example—are extremely difficult to quantify.

Lack of management understanding and support. In one large consumer goods company, the management science budget was cut off after a year's work because the staff had not adequately prepared management for the difficulties involved. Since most marketing problems require considerable computer programming, underestimating the amount of computation involved can often cause difficulties. Successful models have sometimes not been implemented because the management science staff failed to draw marketing personnel into the project.

Inadequate experience. Overly ambitious projects have sometimes been started before mutual understanding and confidence between management science specialists and operating personnel have been developed on more limited projects. A broad marketing problem is not likely to be a good first management science application because it is almost certain to entail more technical complexity and a longer wait for results than management may be ready to accept.

**OPPORTUNITIES FOR THE
FUTURE**

Management science has amply demonstrated its potential for handling problems of complexity, uncertainty, and conflict; and surely, marketing problems combine all these components. Although the solutions to many marketing problems are still quite difficult to work out, there are many indications that the rewards in marketing may well be higher than those in any other area to which management science is being applied.

Starting with known facts about the customer and the company, the demand pattern concept of marketing management interweaves these facts into a flexible system for analyzing the effects of key decisions on net profits. Marketing facts are uncertain because customers' behavior patterns are so variable. This very uncertainty provides both the problem and the opportunity for the marketing executive.

The tendency has been to blame marketing failures on external forces and to credit the successful attempts to creative intuition. But changes in the parameters of demand patterns are not only determined by inspiration, competition, and fate; they are very much influenced by deliberate management action.

Demand patterns can be moved within the limits of probable real-world events. The management science approach can describe these limits with as much certainty as the underlying process will allow. Whether the product is candy bars or locomotives, marketing decisions relating to quantity can then be taken with the assurance that the maximum factual basis is being used to support them.

In marketing, as we noted earlier, the executive is continuously engaged in managing a gigantic experiment. Each event occurring in his competitive world is a datum that will change, to some extent, the shape of the demand patterns to which he has tuned his organization. Management science can effectively help the executive discover new possibilities open to him in his experiment.

Such conditions place a high premium on imaginative, inventive marketing—marketing aimed at achieving the best possible return on a stockholder's investment by various means such as selecting products, channeling distribution, and stimulating customer demand to obtain optimum market shares at minimum cost levels over the long run. How well these tasks are performed will, in large measure, determine the competitive strength of any business.

Analyzing Organization Structure

ORGANIZATION structure, administrative relationships, and individual responsibilities are, of course, altered in proportion to the extent of change of historical methods of operation effected by management science methods. And the systematic development of organizational alignments and communication links to take maximum advantage of the management science and computer-based models can be itself a task for the management sciences. It is perhaps the most difficult of all the jobs to be done, and thus far only the beginning steps have been taken in a few companies. In this chapter, we shall review some of these steps and consider not only what the management sciences can actively do to design organizational models but also how they will affect the current organization structures.

It is commonly noted that the business, economic, and social changes brought about by the even faster development of technology are even more rapidly altering the internal and external environments of business. In response to this changing environment, most corporations are modifying their organizational structures with greater frequency; and trends toward operating decentralization along with centralized analysis and greater flexibility are clearly apparent. However, systematic work is only beginning on the problems of organizational design in a constantly changing environment.

In this chapter, we shall examine possible approaches to a solution of the basic problem of how to organize most effectively to run a business in competitive environments that are as yet unknown. We shall explore one solution: not some ideal table of organization but a new way of building and analyzing any organization.

Effective management requires a rational means of specifying and describing actual or desired organization structures. March and Simon have pointed out that "organization structure consists simply of those aspects of the pattern of behavior in the organization that are relatively stable and that change only slowly." [1] The analysis of such behavioral patterns is the starting point in specifying and describing organizational structure. The *stable* aspects of behavior that make up organizational structure are defined here in terms that may sound strange at first, but basically they stem from the kinds of operational analyses and model development described in earlier chapters. These stable aspects of behavioral patterns include the arrangement and specification of (1) *communication links,* (2) *decision-rule generating processes,* and (3) *reward and penalty procedures.* All of these are generally directed toward the organization's ultimate objectives of growth, profits, public service, stability, and so forth.

As will be seen, such organizational structures are often far from unambiguous. Thus, in the present state of the art, organizational analysis will not completely answer the question of how best to align tasks, decisions, and communications in a given organization. In fact, for reasons that will be elaborated later, this question does not really arise for many organizations that must adapt to a continuously changing external environment (although it may have meaning in groups performing a limited number of largely

[1] See Supplementary Reading List.

routine activities). Such organizations very often cannot be optimally departmentalized. However, as Marshak has stated, "A description of the rules of action and communication that are in actual use in a given organization (though possibly not the officially proclaimed ones) would also help to *improve* them." [2]

APPROACHING ORGANIZATIONAL ANALYSIS THROUGH MANAGEMENT SCIENCE

A systematic framework for analyzing organizational structures is intended to help answer such practical questions as:

- Who communicates with whom, and on what subjects?
- Who controls development of specific decision rules and who applies them?
- How are organizational rewards and penalties determined, and by whom?

Management science approaches to organizational problems are essentially analyses of *decisions, functions,* and *activities.*

Of course, the motivational and other aspects of bargaining, conflict, power sharing, and intragroup tension existing in all organizations are affected by particular organizational and communications structures. However, they lie outside the analysis of decisions, functions, and activities because of (1) frequent individual job changes, (2) rapidly changing business environments, and (3) the need for the development of flexible mechanisms to meet unknown futures. Interpersonal behavior and the meshing of an imperfect organizational structure with the demands, motivations, and requirements of individuals depend upon the skill of the leaders, the availability of resources, the pressures of external events, and the aggressiveness of various parts of the organization. An approach to organizational structure that *minimizes inconsistency of objectives* and *reduces frustration* by rationalizing rewards and penalties can do much to make the tasks of management leaders easier.

It is not the purpose of organization analysis to restructure the objectives, goals, and purposes of the organization: rather, the purpose of organization analysis is to design a "good" organization to fit agreed-upon objectives and goals. To this end, it is not appropriate to assume that the task or functional structure to meet these purposes is also given. In fact, one of the key elements in the analysis is the determination of both actual and alternative task-activity—oriented or function-activity—oriented structures.

In this context, then, the nature of organization as the decision-activity orientation of a group can be examined and the structure described as it relates to *communication links, decision-rule generation,* and *control mechanisms.* It will be noted that any organization has multiple and overlapping structures in the sense that structures vary with differing tasks and objectives. In other words, no matter how neat an organization chart or a communications diagram looks, it does not represent the actual, many-faceted structure of the organization. However, the structure's complexity can be analyzed and reduced to sufficiently simple terms to answer some practical questions of the organization designer.

ORGANIZATION AND THE MEANING OF STRUCTURE

Organizations and their components can be described in terms of the *functions* required to meet their end objectives (e.g., mining, processing, shipping, marketing), the *activities* required to carry out the functions (e.g., purchasing, advertising, designing, selling), and/or the *decisions* required to determine what is specifically done in each activity in response to internal and external stimuli.

To be viable and reasonably effective, a structure designed to carry out specific activities must specify with reasonable clarity the desired end results, outputs of each activity, the rules to be followed in each activity for achieving the end results, and measures for ascertaining whether the end results are being accomplished and the rules followed. In the example that we will use (the simplest possible), there are two activities, purchasing and sales, carried out in two functional components.[3] The purpose of the organ-

---

[3] Note that this simple organization might have only *one* functional component, but even if the function were centered in one person, two separate activities must be accomplished and the description that follows in the text still applies.

ization is to sell as much as possible and to maximize the difference between the amount paid for goods bought and the amount received for goods sold.

There are two separate objectives here; they are compatible (that is, a purchasing activity is given objectives for purchasing that fit with the sales objectives of the marketing activity) if maximum of dollar sales is achieved at the same time that total purchase costs are minimized. And this, of course, depends on understanding and using the nature of the functional relationships between unit sales and selling prices, and between unit purchases and purchase costs. Can this be done without appropriate organizational design? The answer, as we shall see, is "no"—even in this simple case. Therefore, the organization must be properly structured to achieve these end objectives.

This simple description of an organization will serve to illustrate many important points about organizational structure. Note that a structure has not been defined for this elementary organization; *only the activities to be carried out* have been stated. In order to make it "work," the communication links needed, the decision rules to be used, and the control or coordinative mechanism must be provided.

Obviously, only one internal communication link is called for in this simple case: a two-way link between the purchasing and sales functions. But simply saying these two are linked by a communication channel is no better than drawing an ordinary organization chart. The kinds of information to be carried over the channel must be specified. If sales *is permitted* to establish the selling price, it must also know the purchase cost if it is to have some influence on whether the overall goal of maximum profits is met. Also, purchasing must know what quantities of goods sales can sell at what prices and when it can sell them. Thus, a key requirement of sales is the necessary cost information, and a key information item for purchasing is the sales forecast.

But there is still no structure. It is necessary to bring some decision rules into the picture. As with information items that could be communicated, there are many possibly relevant decision rules. Two rules that could be the responsibility of either function will be dealt with: (1) a rule for establishment of selling prices and (2) a rule for establishment of stock levels for purchased goods. There are nine alternatives for generating these rules, even in this two-activity organization. Sales *or* purchasing could generate both rules; sales could generate one, purchasing the other, and vice versa; or joint responsibility could be given to purchasing and sales for one or both decision rules. One cannot know intuitively which of these alternatives is best, i.e., most likely to maximize the difference between selling price and purchase cost and to maximize total sales.

But beyond this set of alternatives, without individual measured controls on the purchasing and sales activities, the organizational structure is not complete and the only assignment of decision-rule generation that could meet the objective would be assignment of both rules to the joint control of purchasing and sales. This, in effect, would allow the organization to degenerate into a nondifferentiated structure in which the control, or objective measure, of the joint function would be the maximization of the difference between selling price and cost. And even this, as we have seen, would require the understanding and careful construction of specific decision rules.

Thus, it becomes apparent that some control mechanism is necessary to complete the organization design. The key control mechanism is, in fact, an output objective or "objective function" for the individual activity, in conjunction with some enforcement —penalizing and rewarding—device. In the two-activity organization described above, the activities can share equally in the net gains from their combination (a true partnership). On the other hand, even in this very simple case it is not easy to determine the kinds of incentives that would maximize the overall gain to both.

A complete structure for this elementary organization can now be examined with simple *decision rules* and *output objectives* indicated (e.g., the purchasing objective is to keep actual purchase cost below or equal to forecast cost, and the decision rule for stock is that it is to be kept at x percent of forecast sales; the sales price decision rule is to sell at 100 percent above purchase cost and the objective is to keep sales volume above or equal to forecast sales).

Though the task objectives and the decision rules seem reasonable in this elementary case, it is not difficult to see that this structure might be far from satisfactory. Thus, the sales forecast furnished to purchasing (note: no decision rules are furnished for making the forecast) must reflect both the arbitrary rule for selling

price and the objective of selling at least at forecast level. Therefore, for safety's sake (and with no management to impress), the
forecast is apt to be on the low side. But the purchase price will
reflect the arbitrary rule for quantity to be purchased and the objective of purchasing at the forecast price or less, and it is apt to be
on the high side—which will push the sales forecast down and the
price forecast up, until they could come into equilibrium at *zero
purchases and zero sales*. So, even the simplest activities and functions can lead to serious problems if the communication links, decision rules, and objective functions are not carefully thought
through.

One way to prevent this kind of result is to provide for another
activity, an activity that will concern itself with optimum decision
rules, activity objectives, and communication links; in other
words, some executive function to analyze and establish the organizational structure. This executive activity must, of course, have its
own communication links and objectives. It quickly becomes clear
that the number of alternatives for each of the structural elements
(not to mention psychosociological relationships of power, motiva-
tion, attraction or loyalty, association, and interaction) is enormously multiplied in business organizations. But an example is
provided by the addition of an executive activity to the simple organization structure we have been considering (Figure 9-1).

The need to recognize behavior as a means of controlling the
output of the organization is, of course, well known. In the usual
bureaucratic description of organization, performance and control
are both outlined in a system of formal roles (or activity areas), and
communications flow through a set of publicly defined channels.
Penalties and rewards are supposed to be known and understood
by superior and inferior. This is generally called the "formal organization," in contrast to the many interpersonal communication
channels, relationships, personally acquired roles, and so forth,
that characterize the actual social group, or "informal organization." However, the usual bureaucratic analysis of organizational
structure fails to deal effectively with the problem of decision-rule
generation (aside from the interpersonal, motivational bargaining
issues that lead to policy statements or constraints on action). In a
sense, the best answer to the practical questions raised earlier is to
(1) examine alternative objective functions for each activity, (2)
examine alternative ways of generating the decision rules to

A Simplified
Organization Structure

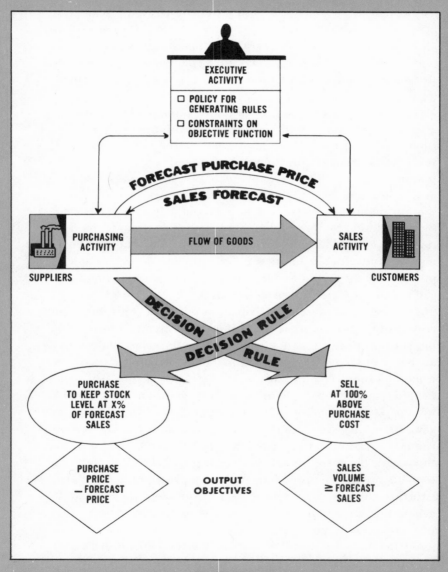

EXECUTIVE ACTIVITY
☐ POLICY FOR GENERATING RULES
☐ CONSTRAINTS ON OBJECTIVE FUNCTION

FORECAST PURCHASE PRICE

SALES FORECAST

PURCHASING ACTIVITY

FLOW OF GOODS

SALES ACTIVITY

SUPPLIERS

CUSTOMERS

DECISION RULE

DECISION RULE

PURCHASE TO KEEP STOCK LEVEL AT X% OF FORECAST SALES

SELL AT 100% ABOVE PURCHASE COST

PURCHASE PRICE — FORECAST PRICE

OUTPUT OBJECTIVES

SALES VOLUME ≧ FORECAST SALES

FIGURE 9-1

optimize the objective functions, and (3) relate these alternative rules (along with the variables to be communicated to the users of the rules) to the overall functions. Once this is done, the decision-rule generators provided for in the structure must be relied on to update the organization's response to changes in the environment.

In summary, the activities of even the simplest organization comprise differing tasks with separate objective functions. To map these out for analytical purposes, an organization chart, or even a manual describing responsibility and function, is clearly insufficient. However, each area of activity can be charted in terms of the main tasks and subtasks involved, and the chart should include statements of needed communication linkages, models or procedures for generating decision rules, and the objective functions the activity-task should try to satisfy. Let us examine how companies fill in such charts and make their implementation effective.

First, it may be noted that large, complex organizations have many goals (and therefore many objective functions) and, of course, many tasks for high-level executives. Like any other component of the organization, these goals will have relative degrees of importance, and their priorities will change with time. The problem of competing, inconsistent, and incompatible goals must be resolved by internal bargaining or by the use of external power. For the purposes of this chapter, this inevitable conflict of top-level goals will be shown to result simply in an agreed-upon objective function or functions against which all other lower level functions will be measured.

The observations and analyses required to complete such a chart of organization structure can now be examined.

DEFINITION OF TASKS AND OBJECTIVE FUNCTIONS

Before decision-rule generators can be established, communication links evaluated, or objective functions determined, it is essential to delineate the tasks to be performed by the entire organization in pursuit of overall goals. This is perhaps the most difficult job of all. It has nothing at all to do with going to someone and asking,

"What do you do?" On the contrary, it requires determining at the very highest echelon what specific tasks should make up the organization's mission.

Once the tasks are spelled out, the first step in the analytical process is determining what the actual (or hypothesized) activity areas contribute to those tasks. The subtask appropriate to a given element may be a decision (for example, in control and re-evaluation, an executive's subtask might be to "approve, or disapprove, any major changes in the program"); an analysis; a communication; or an action in the external world (e.g., letting a contract). The sum of these subtasks, when viewed in terms of each key task, should add up to getting the job done with little or no unplanned duplication (or organizational slack).

Concurrent with the assignment of subtasks, and to some extent inseparable from them, is determination of individual objective functions for each subtask combination. It is often difficult to define the output of a subtask or the contribution of that output to the overall organization goals. One reason for this is organizational memory: the fact that something *has been done* in a certain way—either in the organization under analysis or in another one—perpetuates the feeling that it *must be done* in that way. Although the need often cannot be articulated, because of historical accident and long exposure it tends to be deeply felt. It is particularly difficult to provide objective functions for coordinative tasks such as: "Ensure that pertinent operating command data that would affect status of current projects or would require the addition of new projects are considered during program review sessions." [4] Perhaps it is best to keep objective functions in the forefront but to waive them where they may not be significant—in which case direct control over tasks of this nature will have to wait for long-term, cumulative effects.

Although it may be difficult to describe tasks and objective functions clearly, the discipline involved in thus examining an organization can substantially improve organizational structures for effective attainment of overall goals. And if it cannot be done, an organization may well find it difficult to survive and grow.

For example, one task of a purchasing activity involves procure-

---

[4] Taken from a military organization procedures manual.

ment of materials at specified times and places. The objective functions describe the relative priorities to be given to time, price, and quality, as well as the costs to be attributed to the purchasing activity and to the means of budgeting those costs. Specifying the objective functions makes it possible to develop decision rules consistent with them.

DECISION-RULE GENERATION

An explicit examination of the decision rules in use—and knowing who generated them—is critical for the understanding and satisfactory reshaping of any organizational structure. (The generation of important decision rules through the development of models and algorithms is, as we have seen, the aim of the management sciences.) Those who perform the task must have a clear understanding of how to use the decision rules or models. Otherwise, confusion and conflict are inevitable because decision rules for performing a task are likely to be generated by organization units remote from the task activity.[5]

In the case of the purchasing department, the rules cover methods for determining the number of bids to be received on a particular item, the choice of suppliers to be requested to bid, and the timing of purchase. The way the objective functions are written may, for example, indicate how many bidders will be required. Thus, the more bids that are received, the greater the probability will be of obtaining an item at the lowest available price, but the higher the cost of this subtask. The internal organization of this activity —the allocation of personnel to search out new vendors and to expedite deliveries—is a function of the control system that rewards and penalizes as a result of the value placed on low prices and on-time delivery in relation to the cost of the purchasing activity.

Almost all rules, no matter where generated, are based on partially valid assumptions concerning the reliability of data, on unique objective functions, on models that are assumed to correctly represent the way the world operates, on the assumption that

[5] While it is essential to involve deeply those who carry out activities in the model-building exercises, the key developments for the model are likely to come from outside the activity area.

causal relationships are clear-cut and known, and on some acceptance of statistical order in all aspects of the environment. With all these abstractions from life applied to model building, it should be apparent that we will not find pure optimizing rules for most tasks in the real world.

For this reason, the analysis of organizational structures requires a study of decision-rule generation, as distinguished from a study of the rules themselves. Many organizations with "adequate" decision rules (e.g., set the selling price at twice the cost) have only the most rudimentary mechanisms for generating such rules. In an extreme example, the complex rules of one large organization, developed by the grandfather of the present general manager, are under scrutiny now for the first time in many years.

Decision rules that will serve as guides in future situations must be clearly more general than those developed for present problems. In developing them, one must ask, "What should we do in this *class* of situation?" and beyond that, "How should we structure this organization so that it will react effectively to situations we can only vaguely describe at the present time?" Such mechanisms for generating decision rules often formalize what people learn through experience.[6] To be permanently effective, they must be built into the organizational structure.

To illustrate the difference between a set of decision rules and a mechanism for generating rules, consider two computers: one programmed for routine arithmetic calculations, the other programmed *to learn* to play chess. In the first instance, the program can be permanently fixed: no matter how complex the arithmetic problem presented, the rules for its solution will not be new. In the case of the chess-playing program,[7] the computer can continuously change the basic rules of its play by learning from its opponents: the "superrules" for changing the basic rules are built into the "organizational" structure of the program. And those who program this chess-playing prodigy may wish from time to time to change those superrules.

In the same way, an adequate analysis of organizational structure will determine both "what is" and "what might be" in the

---

[6] Recall the concept of marketing management as experimentation described in Chap. 8.

[7] Called a "heuristic" or learning program.

decision-rule generating activity. And once decision rules can be generated, they must be communicated.

COMMUNICATION LINKAGES

Despite some notions to the contrary, communication in organization structures has little or nothing to do with information theory as it is used in designing and building communication equipment and communication nets. This is because information theory, as theory, is only interested in messages (and their content of meaningless information bits), whereas in organizational communications, meaning is essential. Accordingly, who conveys what bits of meaning to whom and for what purpose must be determined before the effective configuration of "what, from whom, to whom" can be decided. Communication links make it possible to provide activities with decision rules from decision-rule generators, to provide objective functions, and to measure progress against those functions.

Communication includes, of course, the people and mechanisms that measure the state of the key internal and external variables that affect the business. Some decision rules and models indicate what should be done to the incoming signals. Improper sensing, poor rules, and false inputs lead to errors that affect the outputs of the activities using the information.

The decision rules that determine how these activities handle information should cover filtering (the separation of useful information from noise), aggregation and combination of bits of information, and determination of who should receive the various informational outputs. Further, inputs to various activities carry a variety of information: some of it will be used in decisions, some will be used in the objective function, and some will be stored in memory for future use. For example, a requisition from a using activity would not only represent information that would trigger some buying decision rules but would also add to the store of information about the level of work in the purchasing department.

In analyzing communication links as part of the organizational structure, companies have examined the "costs" of information produced and have checked the information to see if it is complete and unambiguous enough to be used for carrying out decisions and measuring objective functions. The nature of communication linkages and their stability represents one measure of the integration of the organizational structure. For example, if operations uses the output of external intelligence-gathering activities incorrectly or deprecates its value, the effectiveness of this part of the communication structure is questionable.

The question of whether communication linkages should be minimum (for speed, correctness, and stability in carrying informational loads) [8] or maximum (for better morale and mutual understanding) [9] can, it seems, be resolved in terms of the alternative task structures, decision rules, and objective functions. There are not enough links if the objective function requires more informational input than the decision rules for the task provide. Conversely, there may be too many links if the decision rules have more informational input than the objective function requires. In a sense, we need to "match the organizational impedance" of the various activities involved in specific tasks. It should be recalled at this point that this discussion is not about corporate organization charts but about the decision-communication links involved in specific tasks. Sometimes the required information is included in other information that a particular donor gives to an activity; this contingency is determinable from the analysis of information needs and use.

SUMMARY

The steps in the analysis of organizational structure are (1) study of decision requirements; (2) determination of the means of generating decision rules, models, and algorithms to meet those requirements; (3) study of actions that have to be taken and of how communication linkages are related to those actions; and (4) study of the objective functions used to control. This step-by-step analysis permits a careful and uniform consideration of the different environments in which the organization may operate. This is particularly important for business organizations, whose continued success is predicated on an unknown future environment. Only by careful consideration of possible tasks and their implications can

---

[8] Suggested by Dubin (see Haire, Supplementary Reading List).
[9] Suggested by Likert (see Haire, Supplementary Reading List).

organization structures be designed to meet such future needs effectively. Using this kind of analysis, one can answer the practical questions mentioned earlier.

One can go much further and begin to refine rules of behavior that will eliminate inconsistencies and incompatible decision rules and objective functions. This approach analyzes the system as a dynamic entity: it considers a series of activities, tasks, and environmental conditions, and determines how the organization will respond to them through its decision rules and objective functions.

But it must be recognized that an organization has to perform many tasks, including some that it was not designed to do. Even a static structure of decision-rule generation, communication linkages, and controls will not completely match all needs. An organization, no matter how large or well structured, is time-bound. Not everything to be done can be done at once, and although rules for determining priorities can be generated, the net result will clearly be less than optimum. Accordingly, the organization structure must allow sufficient slack to accommodate the losses inevitably resulting from sequential decision making and action taking.

A second limitation of this kind of analysis of organizational structures is that complex tasks generate complex decision rules and communication linkages that in themselves may be computationally or mechanically untenable, unstable, or at best highly inefficient. This difficulty can be avoided only by careful task planning and control of decision-rule generation at the highest level. It should be noted that such control often makes for more efficient decentralized decision making and more flexible action than does concentration of decisions at high levels—particularly as a company's operations diversify and become more complex.

There are no absolute answers to the design of optimal organizational structures, and perhaps the nature of social life precludes any final theoretical constructs. Yet much progress has been made in the management sciences, and much that was obscure only a few years ago is at least available for analysis, if not theoretically understood. Precept and exhortation are not an adequate approach to organization analysis and design. The coherent, systematic, and comprehensive approaches of the management sciences can be used for the design and administration of ever more complex social organizations of all types—governmental, labor, welfare, health, educational, voluntary, and military, as well as business.

CHAPTER *10*
Computer Systems
for Management Control

WHILE the management sciences are providing the methodology for more effective administration of complex enterprises, it is computers and computer systems that are supplying the means to put the methods to work. There were over 60,000 computers in use in the United States in 1969, with a total value in excess of $20 billion. It is estimated that by 1975 their number will be almost 90,000 while their value will have doubled, as shown in Figure 10-1. Judging from the accuracy of past estimates, these forecasts are probably conservative. But, by any standard, the computer is here to stay as a fact of business life and as a basic management tool.

The computer owes much of its increasing importance to the almost phenomenally rapid improvement of its capabilities. For instance, the number of additions per second that the machine can perform has increased by a factor of over twenty since 1955, as

160

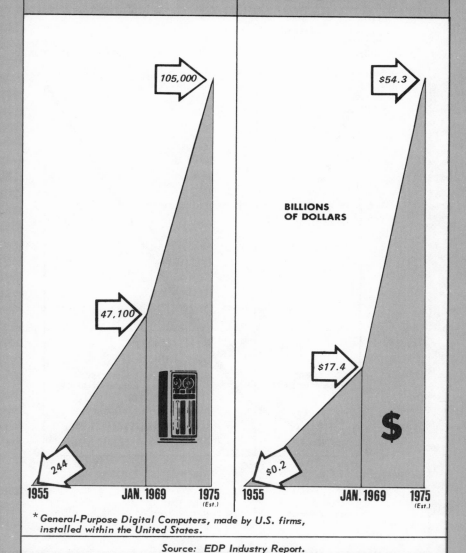

Growth of Number of Computers in Use*

Value of Installed Computer Equipment*

105,000

47,100

244

$54.3

BILLIONS OF DOLLARS

$17.4

$0.2

$

1955   JAN. 1969   1975 (Est.)   1955   JAN. 1969   1975 (Est.)

* General-Purpose Digital Computers, made by U.S. firms, installed within the United States.

Source: EDP Industry Report.

FIGURE 10-1

Computation Cost

**SPEED OF COMPUTATION HAS INCREASED OVER 20 TIMES
WHILE COST HAS DECREASED 25 TIMES . . .**

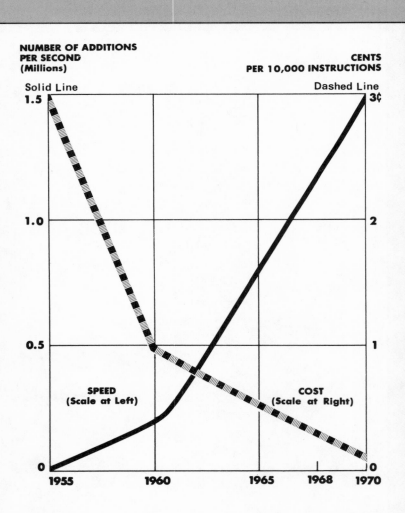

Source: American Federation of Information Processing Societies.

FIGURE 10-2

shown in Figure 10-2. At the same time, the dollar cost for performance of every 10,000 computer instructions has decreased by a factor of about twenty-five. In the process, an array of new staff functions has grown up around the machine: systems analysis, operations research analysis, programming, equipment operation, and hardware and software design and marketing. There are over 150 different job titles now listed by personnel experts in the "systems analyst" category and more than 100 specialized "programming" categories. It is estimated that there are more than 200,000 systems analysts and programmers in the United States today. By 1970, there may be 450,000.

The real significance of these facts is perhaps best illustrated in an outline indicating the computer's course of steady improvement over the past twenty-five years, what the next improvements are likely to be, what is actually being done with the machine, and how it measures up to its tremendous potential.

COMPUTER DEVELOPMENTS—
PAST AND FUTURE

Past computer developments can be said to have occurred in three distinct stages: the period of invention, the period of research, and, currently, the period of development.

The first period began in 1943 when the first real computer (Mark I, an enormously complex electromechanical device) was developed at Harvard University. Somewhat later ENIAC (the first real electronic computer as we know them today) was developed by J. Presber Eckert, Jr., and John W. Mauchley of the University of Pennsylvania. Most of the basic theories of data-processing systems were worked out during the Harvard–University of Pennsylvania development period. For instance, what is now known as computer time sharing (based on the time sharing of trunk circuits by telephone exchanges) was proposed and tried during this period. However, because of the primitive character of the equipment, there was relatively little physical implementation. Components were either nonexistent or extremely costly; one-of-a-kind items and the first peripheral units needed to make the computer practical (e.g., printers or magnetic tape drives) had to be almost entirely hand built. More important, there was almost no market, outside the government, for the new machines. Even if there had been a market, no one had much understanding or knowledge of user requirements or of how to meet them.

The research period, extending roughly from 1950 through 1960, covers the so-called "first generation" of computers and part of the second. During this period, the machines were first commercially marketed and, after a slow start, found increasing acceptance as faster, more reliable, and less expensive components— transistors, magnetic cores, diodes, and so forth—increased computer capabilities and dependability per dollar of investment. Standard electromechanical input-output and other peripheral equipment was produced in quantity, and the first versions of new devices, such as mass storage, optical character recognition, and data transmission devices, were developed. Most of the improvement of systems concepts consisted of refinements of ideas developed in the previous period. Computer programs (software), however, became an important aspect of computer operation. The research period was characterized by rapid obsolescence of equipment as improved machines came onto the market in swift succession.

The development period, which began around 1960 and will probably last into the mid-1970's, is characterized by refinement and extension of existing systems and equipment ideas and concepts rather than by significant innovation. The technology has hardly reached a plateau, but truly new developments are today mostly still in the laboratory stage. However, the period should show some striking achievements. Computers are performing at vastly higher speeds with even better reliability than before. The chief limitation on their performance seems to be management leadership and the development of software, which becomes ever more important as machines get bigger and faster and can undertake ever more complex tasks. The lag between the demands of the users of the new machines and the availability of appropriate software has been estimated at as much as fifteen years.

Current innovations include widespread use of integrated circuits and magnetic thin film memories (first developed in the late 1950s) and the introduction of economically practical small computers. The startling improvements, however, have been in the extremely large memories now available for time sharing.

It is too early to tell what will be the most meaningful new computer developments after 1975 or thereabouts. However, enough is known to pinpoint the following likely development areas: in computers, larger and larger mass-memory storages, character and voice recognition; and in software, perhaps self-learning and self-programming on a scale so extensive that computers will actually "learn" how to solve problems instead of merely following instructions. It is almost certain that the software problem will still exist. Yet it may not loom as important as it does today, due to the development of economic, large-scale integration, semiconductor chips, each bearing several hundreds or thousands of microminiaturized circuitry elements. Used for internal operating functions that are now performed by software, these could substantially reduce the computer's software dependence.

Whether or not a fourth distinctive computer generation is on the way, it seems certain that the current third generation represents a period of relative stability that will last for several years. This is the time when the corporate planner can, without fear of rapid obsolescence, carefully develop the computerized management control system that will best serve the needs of his company and provide a basis for future improvements.

MAJOR DEVELOPMENTS

Computer technology can now provide a business with overall information systems that will give managers new capabilities for analysis, planning, and decision making. Underlying these capabilities are major technical improvements in the areas of computer mass-memory storage and time sharing.

Mass storage

Computer information can be stored in either of two ways—serial or random access. In serial storage, a search for an item of information must begin from the very start of the information file and proceed until the item is located. This is the method used for punched card and magnetic tape. The method is mechanically inexpensive, but it is very slow and unsuitable for any kind of corporate data bank where specific information must be retrieved quickly from extensive files of stored data. In random access, on the other hand, information sought is located by its address code in the information file. The computer does not have to read the entire file until it comes to the right item; it goes straight to the address. This has been made possible by the development of mass storage systems, usually using magnetic drums or disks, that store vast amounts of almost instantly retrievable data.

The development of mass storage devices has been rapid. The first drum storage units built around 1951 had a top capacity of about 36,000 bits of information. Today, storage units with a capacity of several billion characters are available. Fast as they are, however, the new mass storage systems are still much slower than the very fast and rapidly growing internal memories of current computers. This can lead to troublesome delays, difficulties in programming, and inefficient use of these costly devices. However, the improvement in mass memories is still sufficient to allow economical development and maintenance of comprehensive data files dealing with the key elements of a business and its environment. These files provide the basis for the kind of sophisticated and coordinated information systems discussed in Chapters 4 and 7.

For example, some companies are beginning to develop marketing data banks that include sales history, advertising and promotion expenditures, demographic data, and competitive sales information. Properly structured and easily accessible, such a comprehensive data bank provides the basis for advanced analyses of regional and local sales performance, analyses of deals and promotions, and the study of competitive and consumer trends.

In effect, the computer becomes a large-scale data retrieval and communications system with the ability to quickly select and recast information into a variety of decision-oriented formats.

Time sharing

The second major improvement made recently in computer technology was the introduction of time-shared systems that provide direct access and rapid response to inquiries. Along with time-shared computer systems has come the development and use of more powerful user-oriented languages for these systems.

A time-sharing system provides a number of users with simultaneous remote access through an input/output terminal [1] to a

---

[1] Usually a Teletype terminal, but increasingly a cathode-ray-tube (CRT) screen for visual display of data, including drawings and similar information.

large-scale computer system. The computer works so fast that, properly programmed, it can move from one user to another without neglecting anyone or making anyone wait for service. For each user, it is as if his terminal were the only one in the system.

Such systems, of course, benefit the small companies greatly, by giving them access to the power of large computers at very modest cost. However, the use of time-sharing systems is not limited to small companies; in fact, large companies have already grasped their potential for improved management information.

For example, in one large company that has applied time-sharing concepts in the design of company-wide computer systems, a top corporate staff group used the time-sharing system to quickly analyze a recommendation to the chief executive to cut all inventory levels. Over a period of a few days, the group developed a sales forecasting technique and simulation models and used them to perform a series of analyses and to develop projections that clearly showed inventory levels should not be cut. Through time-sharing terminals at divisional and staff locations, the necessary data were quickly assembled, several analysts were able to work with the model simultaneously, and the projections were tested for realism by executives throughout the company. Without the fast turn-around of a time-sharing system, such an analysis would not have been possible.

The significance of these developments is that management is able to test ideas and judgments quickly by directly participating in a dialogue with the computer. The improvement is not simply in speed; it is in the ability to arrive at a better answer by testing and modifying analyses as the problem-solving process takes place.

The computer challenges management to control its application and to use it to sharpen the competitive edge. The challenge is an urgent one, since some companies have already started to widen the gap.

MANAGEMENT PERFORMANCE

In terms of technical achievement, the computer revolution in United States business is outrunning expectations. As a superclerk, the computer has more than paid its way. However, the areas (such as administrative and accounting systems) in which most companies have concentrated their computer activities are also those where the cream (and some of the milk) has already been skimmed. As a result, mounting computer expenditures are often no longer matched by rising economic returns.

This situation is all the more paradoxical in that we have barely begun to tap the real potential profit of computers. Improved end results can most often be obtained through better management information and control. However, applying the new management science analytical methods and computer techniques to overall problems of corporate planning and strategy may not be easy. Such applications require a thorough analysis of interfunctional problems, sound and realistic planning, and adequate personnel resources. Nevertheless, until the computer is put to work where the leverage on profits is highest, lost profits and missed opportunities will continue to mount.

There are three basic questions that the executive must ask in order to effectively apply management science to his company's problems. They pertain to getting the management science and computer system efforts going in the right direction, to allocating resources and setting objectives, and to keeping the effort on course and getting results.

The executive's first question, then, is: "What are the key economic and strategic factors in my business, and how can I use the new techniques to improve decisions in those areas?"

Top-management participation in and guidance of any significant management science project is essential to ensure that the resulting information system will be focused on the critical factors that significantly affect the end results of the business. Top-management guidance is also essential because of the interfunctional nature of comprehensive management information systems. The highly sophisticated, model-based information systems must take into account, analyze, and coordinate not only factors across several functional areas within the company but also the environment in which the company operates. For example, pricing decisions, as we have seen, require information on such factors as direct and indirect manufacturing costs, available plant capacity, total demand, and competitors' actions.

Only senior staff and line executives have the overall perspective to coordinate and focus an effective information system effort. Computer department staffs—though they may be superbly equipped, technically speaking, to respond to management's expectations—are seldom strategically placed (or managerially trained) to fully assess the economics of operations or to judge operational feasibility. The technicians' limitations, incidentally, are raising ever more serious obstacles to the success of new corporate computer efforts. For instance, a technician's "dream" may be a sophisticated computerized accounting system; but in practice, such a system may well make no major contribution to profit. This was the opinion, for example, of the president of a German chemical firm who was asked to approve a proposal for what appeared to be a glamorous new management information system. The system, featuring a desk-side, cathode ray tube inquiry terminal that would display on demand any data from computer files, would enable the president to compare current production figures, by product or by plant or both; it would break down current sales figures in half a dozen different ways; it would display inventory levels, current labor costs and trends, and material costs—almost any kind of operating data he might request. Yet the president turned down the proposal by explaining, "I care more about what will happen five years from now than about what happened yesterday. Anyway, I already get all the routine data I can handle. What would I do with more?"

When management does provide perspective and guidance, the new analytical effort is directed toward solving really significant company problems. One agricultural chemicals manufacturer, for example, has actively begun the development of a management information system to aid planning and resources allocation for its marketing effort. In this kind of business, the analysis of many transactions involving many customers, products, and locations cannot be accomplished without a comprehensive management information system. And it *is* being accomplished.

Another company, faced with competition from many small companies, is developing computer-based information systems for blending raw materials as economically as possible. Raw materials account for over 50 percent of the cost of goods sold; hence, economical blending has a strong profit leverage. More important, however, and playing a key role in competitive customer service, is the ability of such a system to develop low-cost blends that meet customer specifications.

To repeat: management's involvement with, and understanding of, the end results and the manpower and time required to achieve those results is essential to provide adequate guidance and direction to the information systems effort. The payoff from sophisticated information systems can no longer be reckoned in terms of clerical personnel saved or inventory reduced; rather, it must be reckoned in terms of management's estimate of the value of far better ways of making the company's most crucial decisions.

The second major question executives must ask is: "How can we evaluate our overall management science and computer systems plans and keep them up to date?" This involves first assessing individual projects in terms of costs, benefits, and risks—and then assessing how they relate to each other. Each project need not be economically justified in itself: it may be required to provide the base for subsequent payoff work. For example, the development of adequate cost information usually is a key part of a marketing management information system. In many companies, development of such an adequate data base is a necessary first step in the building of a management information system.

Thus, a major task in effectively using the new techniques is integrating projects into an overall plan—fitting the pieces together. An overall plan should be made up of many individual projects that are ranked according to priority and organized around a common set of goals and objectives. The plan would set a timetable for the next five years, outlining results that will provide short-term and intermediate, as well as long-range, payoff. It would outline manpower requirements and resources and set up a schedule for hiring and training personnel. New hardware and new techniques may cause the long-range plan to be modified, but to operate without such a plan is costly and leads to disappointing results.

Obviously, all the management science approaches so far described are implemented by similar kinds of information systems, since each requires certain systematic ways of gathering, analyzing, and summarizing information. Trained personnel can perhaps apply some techniques and run the systems using nothing more than pencil and paper or desk calculators—which are, in fact, adequate for extremely simple applications. Such means could also be considered for applications of moderate or extreme complexity, because the end results may be extremely valuable. On the other hand, the difficulty in achieving requisite accuracy, timeliness, and completeness could jeopardize the successful implementation of any such complex effort. (This is why so many early management science efforts were abortive despite soundly conceived models.) Thus, computers are used not only because they make such work less expensive to do by whole orders of magnitude (similarly, business communications are no longer sent by individual carrier, as they all were once); more important, they make much of the work feasible in the first place. Companies that have successfully applied the new management science approaches have generally made effective use of computers. They have also attacked and resolved the problems of personnel and management understanding and participation.

The final question that executives must ask is: "Given a computer systems plan that has been developed to capitalize on the key economic factors of our business, how do we ensure the success of the plan?" The answer lies in personnel. A capable man is needed to lead the effort. He must be able to win the respect and confidence of top management, to attract competent people to his staff, and to use them effectively. He must understand computer technology but not be infatuated with it. He must make the technology work for the company and not use the company's resources merely to support an elegant systems effort. He must have management's support in developing a program to build up the personnel capability necessary to carry out the plan.

This, in sum, is what is required to make management science really function as an instrument for decision making that is of essential competitive significance to the company, and to realize the method's enormous potential. This is what it takes to wake up the giant and set him to work.

Curiously enough, the problem of effective computer usage does not stem from lack of its availability, capability, or economy. Most businessmen already have computers in their organizations; these computers perform many routine accounting and paper-handling operations. But, as we have seen, these laborsaving devices are capable of performing far more significant functions. To demonstrate what can be done, let us examine further examples of progress and future potentialities in the combination of computers and management science.

EXAMPLES OF PROGRESS

In all the offices of United Air Lines across the nation, the typewriter-style keyboards and video display tubes of some 2,000 "terminals" send and receive vital business information through three large-scale computers. Most of the enormous volume of traffic put through the system—which accommodates up to 140,000 transactions an hour—consists of such operating intelligence as passenger reservations, cargo shipping orders, sales records, and billing details. However, the coast-to-coast network also continuously solves a number of resource-allocation problems in the "real time" of actual operations—among them, aircraft routing and scheduling, aircraft maintenance and overhaul control, cargo scheduling, and assignment of flight personnel (besides keeping accounting records, flashing flight and weather data on demand, and planning and ordering more than 15 million passenger meals annually).

Though United has developed one of the newest of these very large airline networks, American Airlines was the first to install one. Its well-known SABRE system, which performs many of the functions carried out by United's system, cost $30 million to install in 1962 but went into the black in 1964 in terms of direct savings and was reported to have made a net profit of $4 million in 1965. Many other major airlines, including Pan American, Delta, Trans World, Eastern, Northwest, Braniff, BOAC, Air France, and Alitalia, have installed similar systems.

Leading firms in various other industries have introduced similar systems in which a large number of terminals share the working time of today's huge-capacity, ultrafast central computers. For example, to handle data on its 29 million policyholders, Metropolitan Life Insurance Company has more than 800 district-office terminals connected to dual central computers.

Standard Oil Company of Indiana, one of the first firms to use management science models both to optimize automatic refinery operations and to evaluate corporate strategy, recently completed a versatile management information network. The system links managers at each of more than thirty-five operating locations in the United States and Canada with computer centers in Chicago and Tulsa. In addition to its regular bulk of operating messages, it includes an oil movements model deployed by a product transmission subsidiary, Service Pipe Line Co.; well-drilling programs to organize masses of physical and cost data to aid engineering judgment; and strategy guides for policies on developing oil reserves that give optimum answers to such questions as how much prospecting acreage to hold under lease, what level of exploratory effort to mount, and how many trial wells to drill.

To record and plan the most economical movement of all rolling stock, Southern Pacific Railway uses a $30 million time-sharing system that links computers and terminals by microwave radio. This one-company system is due to be supplemented, as we noted earlier, by an industry-wide net that is being developed for introduction in 1969 by the Association of American Railroads (AAR). The AAR's Telerail Automated Information Network (TRAIN) will keep track of all railroad cars in the country, and is expected to increase their utilization by 25 percent—the equivalent of adding another 450,000 cars.

In finance, time-sharing systems with extensive present management uses have been developed. White, Weld & Co., a big New York brokerage house, has mapped out a time-sharing system that makes available at multiple terminals basic financial data on each of hundreds of companies along with a great many programs for analyzing the data relative to investment possibilities. Since 1965 the Ticker-Quotation Computer System has been transmitting reports of all transactions on the New York Stock Exchange. It serves as the data source not only for the trading-floor printers and the ticker network but for a time-sharing system through which up to 1,000 subscribers at remote locations can get, via private telephone line, a machine-generated voice report on the current status of any listed stock. A time-sharing network of special "readers" located around the floor of the exchange also provides the system's input.

Many-layered hierarchies of interconnected time-sharing systems are envisioned as part of a vast development gathering force in banking and finance, a development that a number of popular articles have described as leading to "the checkless society" in America. Officers of the Federal Reserve Bank of New York and of the American Bankers Association have called the development inevitable, and the association has commissioned a team of experts to conduct research on how already existing components would be combined into vast networks so that purchasers could authorize charges on their accounts electronically at their offices, homes, and purchasing points. Clearly, banks, with their regular and continuous exchanges of data with large numbers of corporate and individual customers, are an ideal focal point for the concept of a computer "utility," whereby such customers also become potential users of the bank's large central computers for a host of individual and business applications. Thus, computer power potentially can become as commonly available as electric power, water, or any other utility.[2]

Outside the business world, elaborate time-sharing systems for managing operations have been developed by the U.S. military forces—for example, the Air Force's SAGE (Semi-Automatic Ground Environment) system, which since 1958 has guarded against surprise air attack and stands ready to guide defensive action; the tactical data systems of the Marine Corps and of the Navy (transport and logistical data systems); the Army's master Command Control Information System 1970 (CCIS-70) under development as a consolidation of many existing component systems; and a variety of post-SAGE Air Force systems, such as the Strategic Air Command Control System, the Ballistic Missile Early Warning System, and Space Track for satellite monitoring.

The wide acceptance of time-sharing services is indicated by the rapidity of their growth. In early 1969, time-sharing companies operated nearly one hundred computers serving more than 7,500 terminals, and their number continued to grow at an increasing rate. One of the largest firms in industry, the General Electric Company (GE), estimated that its thirty-one centers served 50,000 people in sixty-one major cities in the United States and Canada. Average GE charges were $10 per hour of use per terminal, $2.40 per minute of computer use, and a varying fee for each unit of data bank storage used. An approximate minimum monthly computer service charge is $100.[3]

---

[2] The time-sharing services actually in operation today are still far different, however, from the "computer utilities" that lie in the future. Such utilities will enable users to have fast remote access to very large computers, along with private (their own or others to which they have legitimate access) and public data banks on a national or worldwide basis.

[3] In addition, of course, to charges for leasing the Teletype terminal, and for the telephone service involved.

As a business in itself, time-sharing service is very much on the upswing. Estimated at over $140 million in 1969, it is forecast to reach $1.0 billion in 1973. Consequently, competition is becoming ever fiercer. Already three of the major manufacturers—IBM, Control Data, and GE—have established chains of time-sharing service centers. In addition, some of the time-sharing companies' biggest customers are entering the business. Major aerospace firms, for instance, whose monthly time-sharing bills run up to $50,000 are considering setting up their own systems to convert this source of expense into one of profits. In addition, switching services presents little difficulty to the customer. Because most services use standard Teletype terminals, a customer has only to dial another number to get a different service. Some big users may subscribe to five or six services, each best qualified for a given job. As a result, a potential subscriber who shops around can obtain service well suited to his needs at reasonable cost.

THE MANAGEMENT SCIENCE POTENTIAL OF TIME SHARING

American businesses are just starting to implement management science techniques through time-sharing networks and computer systems. However, the basic systems along with the needed techniques and economic basis for their use by executives already exist —throughout the country, in diverse forms, and in massive arrays. These large-scale time-sharing systems have grown out of the explosively rapid progress of computer hardware and techniques over the past few years. An equally explosive growth in the use of these systems in business management is unquestionably under way.

Though their management science use thus far is still largely potential, this potential is so great and so decisive for competitive advantage in today's business environment that any chief executive who ignores it is endangering his company. Development is rapid in this area, and some businesses will surely discover that by the time their competitors are reaping the benefits of running management science applications on time-sharing systems, it will be too late for them to catch up.

Four causes underlie the potential of time-sharing systems for improving business performance. First, as mentioned before, they make the benefits of management science methods implemented by large-scale computers readily available to small-scale operations of any kind, whether those operations be independent small businesses or autonomous parts of large corporations. As a result, many small organizations that had thought the new techniques uneconomical will increasingly implement changes in operations along management science lines to try to realize maximum profits at minimum costs. Low-cost accessibility of sophisticated computer services through time-sharing terminals will inevitably bring this about.

The impact of instant, universal availability of computer service on a business (or on an entire industry) was commented on by an executive of Standard Oil of Indiana, following installation of a large time-sharing system:

> Managers of every major department in our company are analyzing in detail the basic functions of their departments, taking a fresh look at their operations for computer purposes. Such analyses reduce departmental functions to their basic framework. This results in the most efficient application of computers, and their most effective use in carrying out these functions better.

Second, use of a time-sharing system to gather, process, record, and transmit all varieties of operating information—production, distribution, and marketing data—for direct operating payoffs automatically provides much of the basic input for management science analyses. The formidable task of first collecting such basic information and converting it to computer-usable form has often been an awkward and costly hurdle for management science studies. But once a time-sharing system routinely compiles all operating information from basic transactions—as in the case of today's airline reservation systems—the initial buy-in cost of applying management science drops, because large amounts of both basic detail data and the significant patterns into which they fall are already in the machine, ready to go.

Third, large-scale time-sharing networks can return profits from on-line application of management science methods and models to improve operating results in the fastest-moving areas of a company's sales. And these systems can prove still more productive for businesses that operate entirely in very fast-moving markets. Consider, for example, a sales forecasting system that one company has installed, which includes hundreds of economic time series, together with a family of analytic programs, enabling the user to develop his own approach to his particular problem. All major sales executives of the company have direct connections to the forecasting system through terminals of their own, as do the principal financial and production managers. Each sales manager regularly compares results for, say, his product line with the forecasts and constantly adapts his marketing strategy within corporate policy inputs to attempt to optimize profits from sales. In addition, interactions between strategies for different product lines are explored and set for fullest profitability; meanwhile, crucial inputs from financial and production centers automatically modify the constantly refined sales forecasts and strategies, while the sales forecasts in turn serve as inputs for shaping financial and production planning. We have seen in Chapter 9 how important these communication links are, even in the simplest case.

As this example indicates, the scale of results that can be attained through optimization techniques is magnified by the capability of (1) a time-sharing system to combine computer power, communications, and stored arrays of operating data, and of (2) proven management science models to quickly serve a widely dispersed management group.

Further, to capitalize on trends, time sharing can reduce the time lags even more between fast-developing market trends and companies' reactions. For example, as we indicated earlier, a manufacturer of highly seasonal style goods found that profit contributions from each price line increased by from 30 to 100 percent for each day saved in responding to demand trends for different styles. Market monitoring through time-sharing networks can cut such a company's response time to intervals as fine as minutes—and can sensitively differentiate market trends in different geographical and other sections—to improve end results still further.

Fourth and last, time sharing converts the computer into a personal tool available and responsive when needed. The implications for management and management science applications are enormous. For one thing, the computer and all its stored, up-to-the-minute operating summaries, analytic programs, and models become, in effect, an inexpensive and extremely efficient laboratory in which to experiment with new ideas. An executive can easily modify programs and data through a terminal directly available to him and his staff so that different approaches can be investigated quickly while previous steps are still fresh in his mind. A manager is thus enabled to play an active, creative, interacting role combining the best of his intuition and experience with the best possible basic information supported by the best management science methods. Managers so equipped will already have taken steps to capitalize handsomely on emerging trends that competing managements proceeding in traditional ways might not even be aware of until much later.

Large-scale time-sharing systems, in summary, have already been extensively developed in limited sectors and applications in business. Today, they are on the verge of finding widespread use in the management of enterprises of all kinds and sizes. Sooner than is commonly expected, time-shared computing in one form or another, from in-house or outside utility facilities, will certainly become the central technology for all administrative activities of American business. And management science models will just as certainly find wide applications through such systems.

The speed with which these developments are becoming reality stresses the urgent need for the majority of executives who have not done so to start developing time sharing and other computer capabilities very, very soon within their own companies. As the next chapter explains, effective capabilities of this kind take years to develop, and such projects face difficult problems. Nevertheless, the effort will prove not merely advantageous but essential. Tomorrow, a company using only present conventional methods against the sophisticated skills of its competitors will have as much chance of success as the searcher in a game of blindman's buff.

The Task for Top Management

IT is clear by now that the computer is here to stay as a powerful tool intimately involved in nearly every phase of the management process. It is equally evident that anticipating new developments in computer technology and knowing how to apply them to corporate needs has become a vital management responsibility, and that the models developed through effective use of management science methods imply the application of computer systems for their effective implementation. Profitable use of management science techniques thus goes hand in hand today with successful development of suitable computer systems. Systems analysis and development has joined the other vital areas of corporate decision making for which the buck stops at the topmost management level.

Has management lived up to its responsibility and realized the computer's full potential? The answer, too often, seems to be "no." Faster, costlier, more sophisticated hardware; larger and increasingly expensive computer staffs; ever more complex and ingenious applications: they are in evidence everywhere. Less and less in evidence, however, as these new applications proliferate, are profitable results from the computer installations themselves.

What has gone wrong? The answer, all too frequently, lies in a failure to adapt to new conditions. While the rules of the game have changed, management's strategies have not.

It is not hard to see how this situation has come about. Less than a decade ago, when applications were simple, management could afford to leave the direction of the corporate computer effort largely in the hands of technical staff people. That time, however, is past. Applications today are not only more complex but also considerably more far-reaching in their impact on different operating departments. Yet the identification and selection of new computer systems are still predominantly in the hands of computer specialists who, despite their professional expertise, are poorly qualified to set the course of the corporate computer effort. The prime importance of new applications is no longer an issue that management can ignore, for it is affected by complex economic and operational questions that the staff specialists are unequipped to answer. Yet many managers, far too many, are still leaving the initiative to the computer professionals. At the same time, they are neglecting their own responsibility for setting the direction of the company systems development efforts.

In recent years, more than one executive has asked, in effect: "Why do we really need computers? Why can't we wait until someone else has developed the applications and then hop on the bandwagon?" The answer, of course, is that the bandwagon is already rolling pretty fast, and the company that waits to hop on is likely to find itself left behind in a cloud of dust. Some companies did start early enough, did develop resources of personnel and know-how, did learn how to integrate the computer with their management processes—and, as a result, already enjoy a significant competitive edge.

The real reason why the computer *must* be used—and used effectively—is as simple as this: If *anyone* uses the computer effectively, then everyone will have to use it or fall behind. In a way, the computer is very much like a new and more efficient production tool. If no one has it, then no one needs it. But if one company in an industry gets it, then all the rest are at a disadvantage until they follow suit—even though the costs of the new tool may be very steep in terms of investment, training, manpower, or management education. All these, of course, are crucial problems in the case of the computer.

As a result of top-management failures to guide the systems development effort in a tough-minded and effective manner, the prime objective of many corporate computer departments is still administrative systems refinement and the reduction of clerical costs. These are the areas where so much work has already been done that the point of diminishing returns has been reached for many new applications. These ill-justified expenditures of money and personnel resources, however, are insignificant compared to the opportunity costs. Though it has transformed the administrative and accounting operations of United States business, the computer has had little impact on many companies' key operating and management problems. Yet, as we have seen, this is precisely where the potential for application of management science techniques and for maximum profits lies.

The computer is an established fact of life—perhaps, *the* fact of life—in most businesses of any size today. Of every $1 million that business laid out in new plants and equipment in 1969, approximately $100,000 was going for computers and associated hardware. For every dollar an average company spends on equipment, it spends close to $2.00 on people and supplies; and the payroll component is rising far faster than the equipment rental bills. Thus, a company that is paying as little as $125,000 a year to rent equipment of very modest capacity is probably spending upwards of a third of a million on its total effort. Most of *Fortune*'s "500" industrial, financial, and merchandising companies have rental bills running into seven figures, and there are also some whose total computer outlays exceed $100 million a year.

Dollars, however, are not a full measure of the computer's significance. Increasingly, computers are affecting not just the cost of doing business but the ways of doing business. The very nature of management is being shaken and changed. The computer's power as a competitive weapon is becoming evident as some companies apply the lessons they have learned the hard way over the past decade. These firms are forging ahead, and it is not going to be easy for the others to catch up.

There is no longer any doubt about it: management cannot ignore the challenge of the computer. It cannot leave all the responsibility to the technical experts. These are lessons of the past. Now, management must learn to look ahead and apply these lessons to three broad areas—technological, managerial, and personnel—that promise to be the most critical over the next decade.

TECHNOLOGICAL

One of the first technological trends that must be recognized is the steadily narrowing cost/capacity difference between computer models of various makes. This does not mean, of course, that the selection of the right system is no longer critical. It still is and always will be, but the choice of equipment available to meet any company's requirements has broadened greatly. This is resulting in an increasing degree of standardization in hardware features and operating costs. These two competitive virtues should be invaluable to the corporate planner. This standardization should, along with computing power, be even more in evidence in the next generation of equipment. However, the real question about this equipment is not how good it will be but whether its users will be able to make it do the things that will bring about the largest payoff.

The steady increase in the machines' computing power represents a second technological trend, as we have seen. Over the past five years, the amount of computing power available for a given investment has more than quintupled. Over the next decade, it is likely to be increased by a factor of ten! We will be getting ten times the present performance per dollar invested in the total hardware configuration, including memory, logic circuits, mass storage, and input/output/display operations. This, of course, means that many applications now considered impractical will become economical. In other words, it is becoming increasingly uneconomical *not* to apply the computer to many production planning, scheduling and control, marketing, forecasting, and facilities planning problems.

Quite a few companies started to do this sort of thing a number of years ago, only to find that they were really "computer bound"

—that the applications were not within the technological capabilities of their current hardware. So their work was, in most cases, unsuccessful. Yet they did gain in other ways. They gained people with experience in dealing with these problems and with the talents necessary to perform the systems analysis and develop the software that must underlie these applications. And now the hardware has caught up.

The third trend that must be recognized in the area of technology is the steep rise of analysis and programming costs. Already, on a national basis, these costs have soared to a point where they exceed the total hardware operating costs—and the end is not in sight. As will be seen later, this situation is aggravated by a shortage of programmers and systems analysts, a shortage that is beginning to loom as one of the greatest problems facing management in the computer area. For the moment, it is important to recognize that developing computer programs is a task comparable in scope to building the machine itself.

Actually, software is the key to effective computer operations today. The development and use of languages, processors, and compilers is crucial. The past ten years have seen the development of a number of important concepts in programming. *First,* man-machine communications are not restricted to machine languages: computer languages similar to the ones used in ordinary problem solving can be developed, thus bringing the man-machine dialogue closer to practical reality. *Second,* it has been recognized that no one language will suffice to cope with the broad spectrum of problems faced by management. *Third,* there is a growing need for a universal interconnecting language. *Fourth,* the ability to easily find out errors in and make changes in programs may be the most important—as well as the most neglected—part of the problem-solving process. *Fifth,* a computing facility is fundamentally an automatic information retrieval system—a system that requires the development of a satisfactory data base before any management application will really work.

The introduction of time-shared computer systems also has substantial future implications, as described in Chapter 10. Management will have faster access to strategic information and an immediate means of analyzing that information. This, of course, does not mean that man-machine dialogues via desk-side consoles are likely to become a feature of life in the executive suite within the foreseeable future. Top management's "interface" with the computer is likely to be nothing more exotic than a telephone, with a human information specialist at the other end of the line. What counts is not the sophistication of the interface but the responsiveness of the computer-based system to management's information needs and the quality and timeliness of the information it can provide. Here, without a doubt, is a major area where realization of the potential of the computer is only beginning.

It should be noted here that intercompany as well as intracompany information systems are fast becoming reality. For example, it is quite feasible for computers installed in the headquarters of a retail grocery chain to communicate directly with the computers of wholesalers and manufacturers. Once the crucial policy decisions have been made, orders and inventory levels will be controlled directly, without direct human intervention in every transaction.

The practical lesson to be deduced by management from these developments is that the chief problem is no longer hardware but "supersoftware." The greatest need is for the skills with which to analyze the total operations of a company in order to develop programs for those segments that are susceptible to interacting informational control.

These technological trends will continue in the next decade. They will bring irresistible pressures to bear on many managements to make effective use of the computer.

MANAGERIAL

What are the managerial consequences of these technological trends—some of the other forces at work that affect the management of the computer effort?

Computer technology permits the creation of an information network which, like the human central nervous system, is not merely a network of communicating cells but essentially a unifying mechanism for the organization of experience. This means increasing coordination of operations, revising the historical tendency toward progressive fragmentation and subdivision of the organization that made mechanization and rationalization of production possible in the past.

Consequently, top management comes under the greatest pressure. As *Business Week* recently pointed out, middle management, far from losing its place to computers, has flourished—thanks in part to the computer itself. But the predicament of top management is acute. In Marshall McLuhan's words,[1]

> The acquiring of new basic knowledge and skill by senior executives in middle age is one of the most common needs and harrowing facts of electronic technology. The senior executives are among the hardest pressed and most persistently harassed groups in human history. Electronics not only requires far deeper knowledge and faster interplay, but has made the harmonizing of production schedules (and marketing introductions and advertising schedules) as rigorous as that demanded of the members of large symphony orchestras. And, the satisfactions are just as few for the big executive as for the symphonist, since a player in a big orchestra can hear nothing of the music that reaches the audience. He gets only noise.

Overriding the challenges of changing technology is top management's growing need to grasp the full dimensions of its own job in the computer era. The chief executive and his immediate subordinates have to learn once and for all that if the computer is to prove a useful and profitable management tool, it must be put to work in the strategic areas of the business. This cannot be accomplished by delegating the problem to technical experts or to trained middle managers. Top management must subject itself to disciplines that until now it has often sought to avoid.

Yet there are hopeful signs of a growing willingness to learn and a growing realization that the job of self-training is only half done when the language and the basic concepts of the new technology have been learned. Some top managers have understood what the pioneering companies have accomplished through computer applications. They are now seeing the problems and needs of their enterprises in a new light and are working to match these needs to the growing resources of computer technology.

Specifically, the experiences of successful managements indicate that the following five propositions are crucial for the full exploitation of the very large potential of computer systems as partners in the management process.

Proposition 1. There exists, explicitly or implicitly, a computer plan in every company. This plan may be to stay out of computers

---

[1] Marshall McLuhan, *Understanding Media*, McGraw-Hill Book Company, New York, 1964, p. 355.

completely, to go after large-scale integrated applications, to tie various elements of business techniques into a tight comprehensive network, and so on. This is not necessarily a detailed installation and implementation plan but, rather, something like the marketing plan, the manpower development plan, the profit plan, or the production plan of a company. The computer plan should be developed and controlled just like any other significant plan. It should include full provision for coordinating corporate objectives, external and internal economies, resources and capabilities, organization, and the current state of the art.

Proposition 2. In developing such a plan, management is committing its company to a course of action that will be binding for some time. For example, some chief executives decided a few years ago to wait out the computer revolution until things were settled and straightforward. They have now found that, for obvious reasons, their decision has greatly complicated early use of third-generation equipment. At any given stage in the progress of a company's managers along the computer systems path, there is a unique time horizon to which they are effectively tied. Consequently, early starts and intensive catch-up efforts can realize a marked advance in a company's time horizon, and hence its competitive advantage.

Proposition 3. The impact of a company's computer plan is felt both internally and externally; it affects both the basic fabric of the company's management processes and the company's competitive position. Thus, a logistics plan requiring integrated inputs from production and marketing can change the way in which key decisions are made in these areas. Likewise, changes in the methods of production scheduling, invoicing, and billing not only affect internal processes but have a direct impact on the customer.

Proposition 4. The classical corporate functional organization frequently hinders the implementation of a corporate systems plan. A corollary to this proposition, itself closely related to the three previous points, is that the computer may make possible a substantially different approach to corporate organization by providing data for common use as well as different kinds of access to information.

Proposition 5. For the foreseeable future, what a company can accomplish with its computer effort in a given period of time will be severely limited by available personnel resources. As a result of personnel shortages, management will have to place increasing importance on *selectivity* in applications, *caution* in projects, and *sharpness* in direction.

These propositions, distilled from discussions with many chief executives, management personnel, and data-processing and systems leaders, suggest why top management is being forced to involve itself increasingly in the examination, approval, and control of computer plans. This represents a great challenge to a conscientious executive. He has found himself engaged in a game where he has had little experience and is certainly not an expert. Let us briefly examine the steps in this game. These are the key steps in the development and implementation of effective computer systems.

STEPS FOR IMPLEMENTING COMPUTER SYSTEMS

Five major steps are required to install a computer-based information system: (1) identification of problem areas and analysis of needed planning, decision, or control models; (2) system definition; (3) system design; (4) system production; and (5) system support.

Figure 11-1 summarizes the tasks required to carry out each of these steps and indicates the ongoing project management functions that must be performed throughout this five-step process.

Step 1—Identification of need. Information systems are developed or changed because management requires better information to strengthen planning, decision making, or control. In some cases this need may be uncovered as the result of an economic analysis of the industry and of the company's position in that industry. In other situations, the need for an information system may stem from a major ongoing function that must be performed. For example, the SABRE system at American Airlines or the credit card system of major oil companies was initiated to carry out important functions in each company as well as to provide information to the company's management. When the problem areas are identified, the role that models should play in the contemplated system must be analyzed.

A Computer-Based
Information System

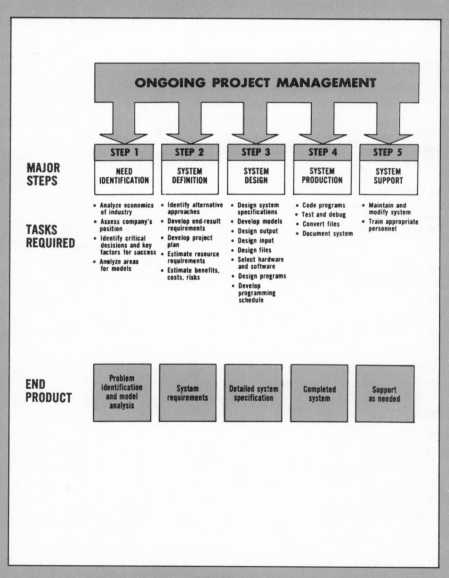

FIGURE 11-1

This first step is completed when the need to develop or improve a computer-based information system has been accepted and when the broad requirements and the models needed for that system have been spelled out.

Step 2—System definition. In this step, the requirements the system must meet are defined and plans are laid for the necessary efforts to meet these requirements. Thus, the activities performed at this time focus on (1) identifying all aspects of the requirements; (2) identifying alternative approaches for meeting these requirements; (3) estimating resource requirements for each alternative; (4) evaluating each alternative's costs, benefits, and risks; and (5) developing a detailed plan for the projects required to complete the work. As we have seen, the users must be deeply involved in this step if it is to be accomplished successfully.

The product resulting from this step is still fairly general. It is roughly equivalent to an architect's rendering but not as specific as the contractor's blueprints. It outlines what the system will do but provides little detail on how it will do it.

Step 3—System design. In this step, the detailed specifications for the system are developed. This process involves: developing necessary models; designing all input and output records; determining the source of data and methods for presenting outputs; determining layout and structure of computer and manual information files; identifying and specifying required computer programs; soliciting bids from computer manufacturers (if hardware is to be ordered); specifying, evaluating, and selecting the computer configuration; and designing the communications network.

Step 4—System production. In this step, in which most of the man-hours are expended, the development of the system is completed. Individual activities include writing computer programs (these may be contracted for from independent software firms); testing each program; testing the entire system; writing procedures for ongoing operation of the system; documenting the computer programs used; and converting information files so they can be processed by the computer.

Step 5—System support. After a system has been completely developed and sufficiently tested, it is turned over to the group that will be responsible for operating and maintaining it. At this point, it may be necessary to recycle back to previous steps so that the entire system, or individual programs within it, can be modified to correct problems encountered during its operation. In addition, this step includes other supporting activities such as training appropriate personnel in the operation, use, and maintenance of the system. If all has gone well, the system is now in full-scale operation.

THE SYSTEMS PORTFOLIO

Determining how to use the computer means assessing the individual computer applications that constitute the building blocks of the entire computer systems effort. Management must have what amounts to a portfolio of applications, each of which has been examined for *return*, for *risk*, and for *security*. There are high-risk and low-risk applications, just as there are high-risk and low-risk investments. Indeed, a computer application *is* an investment— an investment of scarce resources of people, time, and money that, even though small, may have great effect. As in any other investment selection, there should be a preliminary screening step to determine whether an individual application is really worthy of consideration. The application must be seen in light of the key strategic and economic factors and weighed against the remainder of the portfolio. An important application that would require very large proportions of available programming resources, or would take a long time before payout and thus result in other things being neglected, might very well be screened out. The impact of a specific application on other applications—for example, whether or not it will reduce the net risk, increase the security, or improve the net benefits—is critical here.

A crucial issue in analyzing the adequateness of a specific application is the time required to develop and implement it. Another, a generally neglected consideration, is the requirements for involvement of *nonsystems* personnel in the development effort.

It is essential that an estimate be made of the expected tangible and intangible benefits resulting from the application. What profit improvements can be expected from doing this particular job? What are the sources of these profit improvements? How long will it take to secure them? How can the tangible benefits be tested and measured? What are the intangible benefits?

Intangible benefits are often both real and substantial. An executive who wants to know how to use computers should be informed of the nature of the intangible benefits and of the evidence that these intangible benefits are worthwhile. He also ought to have estimates on how environmental changes might affect both timing and intangible benefits. For example, would a faster response to customer inquiries become substantially more important if competition were to take certain actions (as has happened in airline ticket reservations)?

Another frequently overlooked form of intangible benefit or cost is the possible effect of a particular application on the organization structure. Will the proposed application serve to educate management to do a better job? Will it serve as an instrument of change? Will it cause disruption?

Chief executives find these questions worrisome and difficult. They are anxious to have answers that will enable them to understand, evaluate, and approve the overall computer systems plan. Unless they get such answers, they are not likely to supply the support necessary to the plan's success.

THE PROJECT PLAN

The portfolio of potential systems applications should be assembled into time-phased schedules that will (1) observe the priority requirements among the applications; (2) not exceed the personnel and hardware resources that are available in any time period; and (3) in some sense, maximize the net benefits accruing to the organization. This issue is very similar to a job-shop scheduling problem.

Whatever method of choosing, sequencing, and scheduling applications may be chosen to meet these necessary requirements effectively, management must be able to discuss and analyze a number of alternative plans with its computer systems leaders. This is what happens, for example, in marketing and production. The practice is a useful measure of how effectively management processes are being applied to computer systems planning. Since management's commitment to a plan includes allocation of resources, the plan must state resource requirements very clearly and exactly. Top management will then understand that a further decision to change the required resources or the selected applications will change the plan and the expected payoff.

A sound computer systems plan must contain several realistic milestones or checkpoints at specified intervals. If top management is to be willing to commit resources to a major corporate systems plan such as a marketing or a production plan, it is essential for the planner to show how management can check the progress of the plan as it unfolds. A plan with a guaranteed built-in feedback system is far more likely to be accepted than one without it. Thus, a plan should contain milestones at which certain achievements should have been reached and at which progress reports will be made. These milestones serve a number of purposes: (1) they minimize the surprises that can occur when a development effort continues for a long period of time without detailed progress reports; (2) they help management identify the reasons why progress has not been made according to the plan; and (3) when the reasons for unsatisfactory progress have been identified, they indicate what appropriate action has been taken.

Finally, it is common in business planning to have contingency plans, since the achievement of certain goals and milestones may be dependent on factors beyond the control of the systems manager. These might include, for example, the recruitment of systems analysts or the delivery of a software package on a certain date. The alternatives under such conditions should be reasonable and spelled out in advance.

Thorough planning is essential. It has sometimes been stated that the rapidly changing technology and the tremendous uncertainty involved in estimating manpower requirements and benefits make it next to impossible, and certainly not very fruitful, to make a detailed plan for a computer systems effort. Exactly the opposite is true. It is precisely because of the changing technology, the great uncertainties involved, and the difficulties of estimating that it is critically important to develop a comprehensive plan, get approval for it, and control progress against it. To do otherwise is to run the very real risk of having the computer systems activity deviate significantly from the objectives of management and the needs of the enterprise. To do otherwise also presents a risk that top management will not understand, will not get involved in, and will not support the computer systems activity.

PERSONNEL

In terms of immediate practical effects, the overriding issue of to-morrow—and of the day after tomorrow—is neither the technological demands nor the managerial problems just reviewed. The overriding issue is *people;* specifically, skilled computer personnel. They, not the hardware, are the limiting resource. Already the supply is far short of the demand, and the gap is widening inexorably. For the foreseeable future, there is literally no possibility that there will be enough trained people to go around. The shortage will be made even worse by the growing staff requirements of most computer installations. Typically, computer staffs have doubled over the past five years. The department that had 50 people in 1963 has 100 or 115 people in 1969, and expects the number to double again by 1975.

To use computers effectively, three kinds of special talents are needed. First, management science personnel—operations researchers, systems analysts—must lay out the basic concepts of decision making and information flow in the business and determine the means for providing management with critical information about alternative decisions and options. Second, computer systems analysts must apply these concepts to the detailed activities of the entire operation. Third, programmers must take the work of the operations researchers and systems analysts and implement it effectively with the computer. All three, of course, require specialized training, from the Ph.D. degree of the operations researcher down to the special schooling needed by the computer programmer. And all are in short supply.

Not including computer operators, there are perhaps 200,000 qualified computer specialists in America today. (How many of these are well qualified is a moot point; some people contend that perhaps only 75 percent of them are capable of the kind of work that will pay off for management.) A conservative projection of future demands for such specialists is that 400,000 or more of these people will be needed by 1975: each year 30,000 or more will have to be identified and trained.

Moreover, the scramble for skilled computer personnel in private industry is going to be seriously aggravated by competition from another quarter. It has already been predicted that the growth rate of computer activity in Federal, state, and local governments will almost certainly exceed that of private industry in the next few years. This, of course, means a further intensification of demand for trained management science specialists, systems analysts, and programmers in the biggest business of all—government.

Clearly, the competition for talented people will be fierce. And because the shortage of programmers and analysts is going to get worse before it gets better, the chances are that management's use of computer systems five years hence will be seriously hobbled by a lack of competent people to analyze applications and program their machines. Companies leading the field today will, in all probability, continue to attract the best people available, thereby extending their lead. The rich, in other words, will get richer, while the company attempting to build an organization from scratch will find itself at a very serious disadvantage—at least partly because it will have trouble convincing desirable people that it is a progressive company to work for.

But what of the majority? What of the company that, without pioneering, already has substantial investment in computer capabilities and seeks at least to maintain its competitive position in this area? Here is where the shortage is going to hurt most—and where the search for a solution will be most frustrating and difficult.

It is easy to see where the solution does *not* lie. To begin with, it certainly does not lie in pressuring the computer hardware manufacturers to provide more and better training courses. They are hard-pressed themselves. Furthermore, the ability to produce the hardware by no means guarantees the ability to train programmers and systems analysts. Even now, most computer manufacturers cannot do a satisfactory job of training systems personnel for user companies. And the training task is getting no easier. Indeed, the range of new applications opened by the advancing computer technology will, if anything, call for higher analytical skills than have been needed in the past.

If the computer manufacturers cannot be counted upon to solve the shortage of trained personnel for user companies, what are the alternatives? One alternative might be simply to press lower levels of competence into service. But this approach virtually guarantees results of lower quality. It means longer development times and probably, in the long run, much higher costs than would be incurred by paying a premium for top-quality people.

A second alternative is to utilize off-the-shelf or packaged applications. This approach has been only marginally successful in the past because too many of the characteristics of each user company —its personnel, personalities, training needs, forms, procedures, regulatory requirements, and so on—are unique. Techniques and approaches may be transferable, but the detailed design of an information system usually is not.

A third alternative—really the only practicable one, but by no means an easy way out—is *internal development of the needed personnel resources.*

The development of an effective information processing capability, including competent management science personnel, competent systems analysts, and competent programmers, is a long-term proposition. No company, regardless of its size, skill, or intentions, would expect to develop an effective research and development capability in a year or two. Even if the company's very existence depends on R&D, such a capability takes years to develop. Essentially, the talent and staff can be "bought" only in very small increments. This principle applies equally to the development of a strong internal computer capability as it does to R&D. Therefore, management must look upon the buildup of computer systems skills as a continuing, necessary, long-term part of the total job of using the new tools successfully.

SUMMARY

What are the conclusions? As has been seen, three overriding factors define the present situation. First, technological changes in the computer world and scientific changes in the field of management are so rapid and of such magnitude that they blur our vision and perspective. Second, there has been a lack of confidence, understanding, or commitment (or all three) on the part of those users who stand to benefit most by all-out exploitation of the new, aggressive approaches to the solution of business problems. Third, there is an impending famine of trained, experienced personnel, which may prove to be the most critical factor of all in management system development in the next few years.

Nevertheless, constructive action is not only possible but necessary. To begin with, any company hoping to take full advantage of the potential and prospective advances of the management sciences and information processing technology should think in terms of a five- to ten-year program. No shorter time span and no shorter planning perspective will suffice to build up a capable staff, to study potential applications and evaluate their economics, to develop the models, to design the systems, to program, test, train, and convert—perhaps with a hundred or more individual applications—the pieces that make up a coordinated computer-based information system for management.

In a sense, what is involved here is the development, marketing, and application of a highly complex technical product. This development and marketing effort entails so many sheerly mechanical problems of design, training, and conversion to new ways of doing things, that the energy it requires must necessarily be coupled with patience. Attempts to short-cut this development cycle have met with disaster many times in the past and are likely to be even more perilous in the future.

But most of today's laggard companies must make a beginning, and make it soon. Because of the rate at which the talent shortage is worsening, the action the typical company takes within the next year or two can determine its competitive advantage or disadvantage in this area for a long time to come.

The problem of overcoming the personnel bottleneck, in particular, is certain to compel the reexamination of many priorities. Any workable prescription will necessarily involve three basic steps.[2]

1. Begin by hiring or transferring the most capable individual who is available to lead the management science and computer systems effort. Choose a man in whom top management can place its confidence—a man who will attract capable people to his staff and will be able to employ them effectively.

[2] These steps are described on the assumption that management science and computer systems are part of the same organizational function. This is likely to be the best alignment, but if the systems are separate functions, these steps should be applied to each.

2. Provide the function with high organizational stature and top-level relationships. Because of the function's interfunctional impact and its potential importance to the chief executive, the manager in charge of management sciences and computer systems must report directly to him.

3. Give optimum support to planning, staffing, and implementing a long-range program of management information and decision-making applications. Adjust the computer systems plan as necessary to reflect new and better hardware, new areas of interest to the company, and advances in the techniques of system design. But do not try to operate without a plan. This will almost certainly mean being forced into a reactive posture that will prove in the future—as it has in the past—to be both futile and costly.

Companies that might be tempted to hold back and wait for the situation to stabilize should examine the facts carefully. There is no reason to think that stability is anywhere in sight. It seems most unlikely, in fact, that the management-sciences information-processing technology will ever be stable enough to make decisions comfortable. But this situation is not, after all, different in kind from others that top management has learned to conquer, or at least to cope with, in the past. In a sense, the chief executive in business faces similar dynamic problems every day. To be sure, the problems brought on by the emergence of these new fields are exceptionally severe. But the search for an adequate solution is not a search for a fixed object. It is a search for a temporary adjustment, a balance between uninspired stability and unnecessary risk. This balance must be sought in a medium of rapid flux. But flux, after all, is the medium in which the greatest management victories are achieved.

Supplementary Reading List for Executives

Ackoff, Russell L., and Patrick Rivett: *A Manager's Guide to Operations Research*, John Wiley & Sons, Inc., New York, 1963.

The title describes this book perfectly. The book is nonmathematical and the authors are leaders in the field. The exposition is clear and the book is filled with examples drawn from the experience of the authors.

Beer, Stafford: *Decision and Control*, John Wiley & Sons, Inc., New York, 1967.

This book presents the author's ideas about the future developments of operations research and the implications of this development for business and society. It uses no mathematics whatsoever. However, the reader will find that it requires constant, careful thinking to follow the argument.

Burck, Gilbert: *The Computer Age*, Harper & Row, Publishers, Incorporated, New York, 1965, 148 pp.

198

A nontechnical examination of the impact of computeriza-
tion on management and its future possibilities in factory and
office. Explains why the computer is not likely to outwit man
and concludes that human decision makers teamed with the
computer have almost limitless potential. Also discusses the
computer industry and particularly IBM's position in it. This
material appeared as a series of articles in *Fortune*.

Bursk, Edward C., and John F. Chapman, editors: *New Decision-Making
Tools for Managers*, Harvard University Press, Cambridge, Mass., 1963, 413
pp.

Seventeen articles selected from the *Harvard Business Review*,
most of them published since 1959 and most of them dealing
with mathematical programming in business situations.
Ranges from such general topics as econometrics and operations research to tests of test marketing and diversification
strategies.

Churchman, C. West: *Challenge to Reason*, McGraw-Hill Book Company,
New York, 1968.

This is a fascinating look at the philosophical problems involved in the rational approach to complex decision making.
The book requires careful thought, but the reader will be re-
warded by a much clearer understanding of the necessary
limitations of rational decision analysis.

Cross, Hershner, and others: *Computers and Management*, The 1967 Leather-
bee Lectures, Harvard University, 1967.

This series of five lectures discusses the impact of computers in
management. The problems, including data handling and
economics, are analyzed in terms of the individual experiences
of the five prominent businessmen who served as lecturers.

Dorfman, Robert, editor: *Measuring Benefits of Government Investments*, The
Brookings Institution, Washington, D.C., paperback, 1965.

These are the papers given at a conference on cost-benefit
analysis. This kind of analysis, sometimes called cost-
effectiveness analysis, is of major use when it is extremely difficult to quantify the worth of the outcomes of the various
courses of action which are available. The book has many examples of this kind of problem and methods for handling it.
Most of the examples are drawn from the public area, but the
methods discussed are of general interest to business
executives.

Emory, C. William, and Powell Niland: *Making Management Decisions,* Houghton Mifflin Company, Boston, paperback, 1968.

This fine book presents many of the explicitly mathematical techniques of operations research without using any mathematics at all—and does it successfully. In addition, there are five excellent preliminary chapters on formulating OR problems properly.

Fulcher, Gordon S.: *Common Sense Decision Making,* Northwestern University Press, Evanston, Ill., paperback, 1965.

This is a completely nonmathematical, very short exposition of the basic ideas of a rational approach to decision making. It is a particularly clear statement of the essentials of decision analysis and it is illustrated by examples drawn from public policy.

George, Claude S., Jr.: *The History of Management Thought,* Prentice-Hall, Inc., Englewood Cliffs, N.J., 1968.

This interesting presentation of the history of management thought from ancient times until the present is useful, since it gives some much needed perspective on how we arrived at our present approaches to decision making.

Haire, Mason, editor: *Modern Organizational Theory,* John Wiley & Sons, Inc., New York, 1959.

This book contains papers by a number of experts on the subject of organization, most of which should be of considerable interest to executives. The theories of organizational behavior that are offered are largely industrial and include consideration of the conflicts within organizations and problems of decentralization. The articles of Dubin and Likert mentioned in Chapter 9 are particularly appropriate for executives interested in analytical approaches to organization problems.

Higginson, M. Valliant: *Managing with EDP,* American Management Association, New York, 1965, 111 pp.

A nontechnical treatment of EDP written for executives. Provides basic information about computer applications and relates these applications to the overall process of management. Does not discuss the management of an EDP department and does not summarize company practices. Concerned instead with concepts, problems, and attitudes about EDP in relation to management.

Kaufmann, Arnold: *The Science of Decision Making*, McGraw-Hill Book
Company, New York, paperback, 1968.

This excellent book surveys and exemplifies most of the well-
known methods of quantitative analysis and a good deal more
besides. Little mathematics is used (but a reader unfamiliar
with mathematics may find the use of mathematical symbols a
little heavy). There are many clear, well-chosen diagrams to
illustrate the arguments. The many chapters without any
mathematics may be read by themselves if necessary.

Kepner, Charles H., and Benjamin B. Tregoe: *The Rational Manager*,
McGraw-Hill Book Company, New York, 1965.

This book presents a systematic approach to problem solving
and decision making. The material it covers precedes the use
of quantitative methods in a specific decision problem. The
authors include a variety of examples which demonstrate the
need for the kind of approach they suggest.

Lyden, Fremont J., and Ernest G. Miller, editors: *Planning-Programming-
Budgeting: A Systems Approach to Management*, Markham Publishing
Company, Chicago, paperback, 1968.

This collection of readings about the Planning-Programming-
Budgeting system that President Johnson ordered should be
used by all Federal agencies after its famous success in the Defense Department. It provides an excellent background in this
relatively new area that has many implications for the
businessman.

March, J. G., and H. A. Simon: *Organizations*, John Wiley & Sons, Inc., New
York, 1958.

This is one of the best books on organizational theory. It includes a brief summary of classical concepts starting with Tay-
lor's views of scientific management. It describes the constraints on effective operation within organizations and discusses group participation and conflict. The book concludes
with a helpful discussion of the development and encourage-
ment of innovation.

Miller, David W., and Martin K. Starr: *The Structure of Human Decisions*,
Prentice-Hall, Inc., Englewood Cliffs, N.J., paperback, 1968.

This nonmathematical book examines the range of decision
problems from the point of view of an integrated decision theory. The authors try to demonstrate the underlying unity of a
variety of approaches to decision problems.

Quade, E. S., and W. I. Boucher, editors: *Systems Analysis and Policy Planning*, American Elsevier Publishing Company, New York, 1968.

This collection of lectures given by the RAND Corporation to high-ranking military officers deals with rational approaches to top-level decision problems—specifically, ones where it is not even clear what the objective ought to be. While the examples in this book come from defense problems, the methods are of unusually great interest for general executives.

Raiffa, Howard: *Decision Analysis*, Addison-Wesley Publishing Company, Inc., Reading, Mass., paperback, 1968.

This book is a masterpiece of exposition covering decisions under uncertainty. The author deals with the entire subject: measurement of utilities, use of subjective probabilities, decision trees, and so forth. Only algebra is used and the author has a very pleasant, informal style.

Shuchman, Abe, editor: *Scientific Decision Making in Business*, Holt, Rinehart and Winston, Inc., New York, 1963, 568 pp.

An introduction to operations research for nonmathematicians, consisting of fifty-two selections. It describes the aims and methodology of OR and in the last selection applies them to production management, marketing management, and financial management. A good elementary collection demanding only a knowledge of beginning high school algebra.

Sisson, Roger L., and Richard G. Canning: *A Manager's Guide to Computer Processing*, John Wiley & Sons, Inc., New York, 1967.

This book describes how computer systems fit into a business, how they are designed and organized, and how they relate to other functions of a business. It presents a way of categorizing information for management purposes and among its many features includes explanations of computer terminology in management language. This book also contains an excellent bibliography.

Solomon, Irving I., and Laurence O. Weingart: *Management Uses of the Computer*, Harper & Row, Publishers, Incorporated, New York, 1966, 224 pp.

A nontechnical book offering guidelines for management planning and use of the computer for business data processing. Gives broad descriptions of computer capabilities, explains the goals and procedures of the feasibility study, and describes the development and implementation of a computer system.

Index

Accounting:
  cost, 4–5
  double-entry bookkeeping, 19–20, 26
Activities of organizations, analysis of, 147, 153–154, 157
Activity sequencing, 10, 11
Advertising, 6n., 22, 130–131, 136–137
Aerospace industry, 108, 175
Air France, 172
Algebra, 8, 9
Algorithms, 17–28, 36, 107, 109, 117, 119, 155
  defined, 18
Alitalia Airlines, 172
Alternatives, 26
  analysis of, 49
  quantification of, 21
  and restraints, 23
American Airlines, 172, 187
American Association of Railroads, 111
American Bankers Association, 173

Anheuser-Busch, 133
Arnold, Matthew, 21
Association of American Railroads, 173
Automobile industry, 2, 107–108
Average annual return on investment, 67, 88–89, 100

Bamberger's department store, 6n.
Behavioral sciences, 5
"Best-guess" analysis, 58, 62, 69, 71, 73, 79, 82, 85, 141
Biological sciences, 5
BOAC, 173
Braniff International, 172
Bristol-Myers, 131
Brown, Arthur, 6n.
Business Week, 185

Canada, 172, 174
Capital investment decisions, 2, 10, 25, 33, 38–39, 46, 66–85
  cost analyses, 80

Capital investment decisions (*Cont.*)
  rate of return on investments: as criteria, 92, 100
    and cutoff rates, 74, 88
    techniques for estimating, 67–68, 86, 88, 92
    and risk analysis, 66–85
    and time, 67
    (*See also* Investment policy)
Carnegie-Mellon University, 7*n.*
Case Institute of Technology, 7*n.*
Chemical industry, 109–112, 169
Chicago, Illinois, 172
Churchill, Winston, 6
Columbia University, 7*n.*, 118
Commercial banks, 174
Communications links, 146, 148, 149, 151, 153, 157–158, 177
  adequacy of, 158
  and people, 157
Competitors, actions of, 107
Computer specialists:
  government competition for, 194
  shortage of, 193–195
  training of, 194, 195
Computer systems, 4, 5
  evaluation of applications, 190–191
  examples of, 172, 173
  implementation of, 187–190
  and need for trained people, 193–197
  planning applications, 191–192
  (*See also* Management information systems)
Computer utilities, 174
Computers:
  benefits of, 87, 169–170, 190–191
  capabilities of, 49, 160, 164, 183
  and competition, 180–182, 186
  consequences for management, 184–187
  corporate expenditures on, 181
  ENIAC, 163
  evaluation of applications, 190–191
  extent of use, 46
  history of development, 163–165
  importance of, 160, 181
  and management leadership, 164–171, 179–180, 184–187, 190–192, 195
    failures of, 181–182, 195
    and limitations of technicians, 169, 180, 182
  Mark I, 163
  and mass information storage, 165–166
  memories of, 163–164

Computers (*Cont.*)
  number and value in the U.S., 160
  profitable use of, 168, 171, 180, 181, 185–187, 190
    plan for, 191–192
  small, 164
  software, 164–165, 183
  as superclerks, 167–168, 170, 181
  technological trends in, 182–184
  time-sharing (*see* Time-sharing)
  use of, 26, 27
    in evaluation of investment policies, 98
    in risk analysis, 79–80, 82
  use of terminals, 131
  user costs of, 163, 182, 183
  and user-oriented languages, 183, 166
Consumer goods industry, 114–130, 136, 139
Continental Oil, 2
Control Data, 175
Control mechanisms, 32–33, 146, 148–151, 155, 158
  objective functions, 150, 153–155
  rewards and penalties, 150
Cost-benefit analysis, 8
Credit card systems, 173–174, 187
Critical path scheduling and methods (*see* Network analysis)
Customer service, 133–134, 141

Dantzig, George, 119
Decision making, 12, 15–29
  automation of, 27, 28
  and constraints, 23, 53
  coordination in, 137
  and decision rules, 92, 112
  key factors in, 20
  and models, 20
  procedures for, 114
  quantification in, 17, 19–21
  role of management in, 27–28, 33, 45, 62, 105
  rules for, 151, 153, 156, 158
    and the future, 156
    and implicit assumption, 155–156
    incompatability of, 159
  strategic, 46
Decision-rule generation, 146–149, 153, 155–158
  computer example of, 156
Delta Air Lines, 172
Demand patterns, 143
  defined, 138
  efforts to change, 138, 141
  and optimization, 138

Depreciation, 98
Discounted cash flow analysis, 68, 80, 89, 92, 100
Distribution and distribution systems, 40–43, 106–129, 133
Dividend policies, 98
Du Pont Company, 131

Eastern Airlines, 172
Eckert, J. Presber, Jr., 163
Efficiency frontier, 96, 98, 100
Efficiency of investment policies, 95–105
Electronics industry, 132
Environment, 158
  change in, 145–146
  economic, 49–51, 133
    models for, 53
Estimates:
  adjustment of, 74
  errors in, 24–25
  and experts, 78
  forcing the outcome to fit, 75
  three-level, 74
  and uncertainty, 86–87
Executive talent, 22
Expected return, 73, 76, 82, 96
  (*See also* "Best-guess" analysis)
Exponential smoothing, 133

Federal Reserve Bank of New York, 173
Financial decisions, 50
  models for, 53–54
  pro forma statements, 53–54
Ford Motor Company, 3
Forecasting, 10, 11, 38, 42, 73, 133
  economic, 2
  of sales, 2, 132, 150, 167, 177
Fortune's "500," 181
Functions of organizations:
  analysis of, 147, 153–155
  and historical precedent, 154
  integration of, 112
  and measuring progress, 157
  and optimizing, 156
  and organizational slack, 154

Garment industry, 132
General Electric Company, 174, 175
General Foods, 131
General Motors, 3, 131
General Tire and Rubber, 3
Great Britain, 6, 7

Harvard University, 163
Heinz, H. J., Company, 2
Hughes, Charles Evans, 23

IBM, 175
Information, 30
  costs of, 32, 157
  importance of, 13
  improvement in, 32
  need for, 142, 168, 183
  (*See also* Management information systems)
Information theory, 157
Institute of Management Sciences, 7n.
International Harvester, 3
Inventory control, 8, 107, 109, 133, 137
  seasonality, 109
Investment banking industry, 173
Investment policy:
  alternative policies evaluated, 96–105
  components of, 92
  criteria for selection of investments, 92–95
  determinate, 93, 99
  effectiveness of, 95–96
  example of, 93–94
  functions of, 92–94, 96
  management science approach, 105
  risk-based, 93–94, 99
  (*See also* Capital investment decisions)

Kennedy, John F., 33

Levenson, Harold, 6n.
Linear programming, 5, 9, 10, 26, 53–54, 109, 115
  executive understanding of, 126
  in production, distribution, and marketing analysis, 117–123
  profitable use of, guidelines for, 126–128
  prototype models, 119–124
Lockheed Aircraft, 2
Logistics (*see* Distribution and distribution systems)
Long-range planning (*see* Strategic planning)

McLuhan, Marshall, 185
McNamara, Robert S., 3
Management information systems, 22, 30–33, 108, 112, 114, 168

Management information systems
    (*Cont.*)
  and computer memories, 165–166
  cost of, 43
  dangers in, 45
  data for, 170
  and decision making, 170
  examples of, 169
  implementation of, 43
  installation of, 187–190
  integration with management science
      methods, 114
  oversophistication of, 169
  and policy alternatives, 41–43
  role of management in, 168–169
  (*See also* Control mechanisms; Opti-
      mization models; Real-time sys-
      tems; Simulation)
Management science, 1–14
  applications, examples of, 2, 3, 6, 8, 10,
      11, 16, 17, 23, 26, 32, 35–37,
      47–56, 118, 123–128, 138,
      176–177
  and competition, 15, 28–29, 45, 129,
      138, 144, 175, 196–197
  and computers, 1, 46, 160–197
  without computers, 170–171
  defined, 4
  development of application, 5
  development of capability within a
      firm, 12–14, 195–197
    competent personnel, 13, 142, 171
    overall plan, 170
    top-management involvement, 14
  effect on organization structure, 145
  effectiveness of, 4
  evaluation of a company's efforts, 170
  executive training in, 117
  growth of, 4
  historical background, 4–7
  and intuition, 15–16, 23
  in investment decisions, requirements
      for use of, 105
  and marketing: benefits and prob-
      lems of, 141–144
    examples of application, 130, 132–
      134, 136–138
  methodology of, 5
  organization of a study, 115–117,
      123–125
  and people, 5
  in production, distribution, and mar-
      keting, guides for use of, 128–
      129
  and recessions, 31–32

Management science (*Cont.*)
  role of management in, 115–117,
      126, 128–129, 142, 168–171, 181,
      195–197
  and scientific research, 5
  and small companies, 3, 13, 167, 176
  in solving a combination of problems,
      137
  team approach, 115–116
  techniques, 7
    integration of, with information
      systems, 114
  and universities, 7
Manpower, levels of, 109, 123
Manufacturing, 108
March, J. G., 146
Marginal costs and benefits, 27
Marketing and marketing systems, 3,
      47, 50, 75, 106–144
  "best mix" of sales, advertising, and
      promotion, 136
  and competitive activity, 131–132
  coordinated systems, 137
  information system, 139
  and intuition, 143
  management science approach:
    advantages of, 141, 143, 144
    problems of, 142
  and minimum order size, 122
  model of market structure, 139
  as an ongoing experiment, 139, 143
Marshak, J., 147
Mass. Institute of Technology, 7*n.*
Mauchley, John W., 163
Media selection models, 131
Merchandizing, 6*n.*, 36, 37
Metropolitan Life Insurance Co., 172
Military problems, 6, 7, 33, 108
Models and model building, 2, 8, 10, 20–
      21, 46, 107–109
  and decisions, 53, 54, 155
  of demand data, 115
  environmental, 53
  financial, 53, 54
  importance of, 43
  and investment policy, 98–99
  probabilistic, 53
  in production, logistics, and market-
      ing, 106–144
    examples of, 107–112, 119–121,
      123–128
    input detail, 128
    model developed, 112–129
    new applications of, 128
  for strategic planning, 52

Net present value (*see* Present worth analysis)
Network analysis, 2, 5, 108
New products (*see* Product-line planning)
New York, 173
New York Stock Exchange, 173
Newark, New Jersey, 6n.
Northwest Airlines, 172
Northwestern University, 7n.

Office equipment industry, 133
Oil industry, 3, 26, 27, 172, 173, 176, 187
Operating decisions, 50
  models for, 53–54
Operations research, 4–6, 8, 163
Operations Research Society of America, 7n.
Optimization models, 33, 40–43, 115, 119, 122, 177
  development of, 42
  of nutritional diet, 118
Organization structure, 145–159
  analysis of: using management science, 145, 147–148
    and competition, 154, 158
    purpose of, 148
    steps in, 158
  bureaucratic description of, 151, 153
  centralization and decentralization, 146, 159
  and computer applications, 186, 191
  defined, 146
  described, 148
  informal, 151, 156
  and organization goals, 146, 153, 159
  role of management in establishing, 151, 154, 159
  (*See also* Activities of organizations; Communications links; Control mechanisms; Decision-rule generation; Functions of organizations)

Pacioli's algorithm, 19, 20
Packaging, 131
Pan American, 172
Payback period, 67, 88, 89, 92, 100
PERT, 2, 108
Physical sciences, 5
Planning and control, 108, 112
  (*See also* Control mechanisms)
Plant expansion, 48

Polaris Weapon Systems, 108
Present worth analysis, 68, 92, 100
Pricing policies, 134
Probabilistic estimates, use of, 58, 62, 78–79, 87
Probability theory, 8, 9, 24, 25
Processing of raw materials, 47
Product-line planning, 132, 137
  new product evaluation, 2, 48
  product life cycle, 141
Production, 47, 106–129
  scheduling and control, 2, 3, 107
Programming:
  developments in, 183
  employment in, 163
  mathematical, 2, 4, 5, 10
  (*See also* Linear programming)
Promotion, 136–137
Purchasing, 107, 108, 137, 149, 154–155

Quality control, 5
Quantification, 21–22
  factors difficult to quantify, 22, 92
  factors readily quantifiable, 22
Quantitative methods, 4, 17
Queuing theory, 5, 111

Railroad industry, 136, 173
Raytheon, 2
Real-time systems, 32, 34–37
  applications of, 35, 36
  cost of, 35, 36
  defined, 34
  and objectives of decision maker, 35, 36
Research and development, 22
Resources:
  acquisition of, 10, 11
  allocation of, 10, 11, 26, 172
Risk:
  attitudes toward, 94
  explained, 57–58, 71
  and return, 89, 100, 102
  (*See also* Uncertainty)
Risk analysis, 37–39, 56–85, 87, 112
  and capital investment decisions, 66–85
    compared to other techniques, 77–85
    input factors, 77–78, 80
  examples of, 58–62, 65, 73, 77–85
  and investment policy, 93–105
  profiles, 65, 85, 89, 93, 98, 103

Risk analysis (*Cont.*)
  questions answered by it, 89
  and sensitivity analysis, 82, 85
  steps in, 76
  when useful, 65, 85
Routing problems, 2, 172

Sales, 131, 136, 137, 149
Scheduling, 172
  of equipment, 109
Scott Paper, 2
Search theory, 5, 7
Sensitivity analysis, 62, 82, 85, 87
  example of, 65
Service Pipe Line Company, 173
Simon, H. A., 146
Simulation, 25, 33, 37–39, 112, 134,
    167
  benefits of, 103–105
  to evaluate investment policies, 98
  and risk analysis, 76, 82, 87, 96
  steps in, 39
SKF Industries, 2
Small companies, 138, 176
  development of management science
      capability, 12–14
  and time-sharing, 167
Southern Pacific Railway, 173
Standard Oil Company of Indiana, 172,
    173, 176
Stanford University, 7n.
Statistical inference, 8, 9, 24, 25
Stigler, George, 118
Strategic planning, 46–62
  and alternatives, 49
  computer model for, 52
  defined, 48
  end results, 54
  examples of, 47–56
  and management science, examples
      of application, 47–51
  steps in, 49–52
  and uncertainty, 49
Systems analysis, 2, 8, 163
  and decision making, 114
  employment in, 163
  of production, marketing, and distri-
      bution, 106–112
  benefits of, 114, 123–129

Systems analysis: of production, mar-
    keting, and distribution (*Cont.*)
  coordinated system developed,
      112–129
  guidelines for, 128
  role of management, 117
  steps in, 123–125
  work plan for, 115–117, 124

Time-sharing, 163–167, 173, 174, 183
  benefits of, 175–177
  and competition, 175, 178
  competition in, 175
  examples of, 167, 176–177
  growth of, 174–175, 178
Trans World Airlines, 172
Tulsa, Oklahoma, 172

Uncertainty, 23–25, 38–39, 46, 68, 87,
    89
  methods of coping with, 73–75
  (*See also* Risk; Risk analysis)
United Air Lines, 172
United States, 7, 160, 172, 174
U.S. Air Force, 174
U.S. Army, 174
U.S. Department of Defense, 34
U.S. Marine Corps, 174
U.S. Navy, 6, 108, 174
U.S. Rubber, 3
U.S. Steel, 131
University of California, 7n.
University of Pennsylvania, 7n., 163
Utility industries, 16–17, 21

Variability, 76, 95, 102–103
  control of, 103

Waiting line theory (*see* Queuing the-
    ory)
Warehousing, 107, 109, 115, 119, 121,
    133
Westinghouse, 131
White, Weld & Co., 173
Work plan for a systems analysis study,
    115–117
World War II, 6, 17